More praise for
'Do you want to

'As a Parliamentarian, I can tell you straight up that truth-telling on climate has been the political game-changer, these past few years. Through the Green Party, in Extinction Rebellion that he helped to launch, in the Greens' "Climate Activist Network", and now in the new "moderate flank" he is co-creating, Rupert Read has been a crucial thought-leader, again and again ahead of the curve. This book is his testament on what it means in the 2020s to live in truth. Some of what he says is uncomfortable reading, including for me; but that is always the way, with inconvenient truths. Please read this book to be provoked and pushed into action. We are being *called* by the crisis whose fault-lines Read startlingly delineates, as we have never been called before. It's past time for us to heed the call.'

– Elizabeth May MP,
Parliamentary Leader of the Green Party of Canada

'In 1940 Winston Churchill had nothing to offer but "blood, toil, tears and sweat". He did not lie to the people, and British society fought for peace, prosperity, and freedom, knowingly. The truth about the ongoing climate and ecological disasters, and the risks of societal collapse, is hard to accept. Yet we must go through it to save lives. In this humble, sincere, and quick-witted book, Rupert Read invites us to find courage, stop being afraid of fear, and trust people without infantilising them. It's time to get serious about mass mobilisation as Rupert does, with compassion, love, rage, and authenticity.'

– Pablo Servigne & Raphael Stevens, creators of collapsology
and collapsosophy, authors of *How everything can collapse*
and *Another end of the world is possible*

'As Rupert Read says, "This is a book for everyone" – a deeply *invitational* book, not offering certainty but glimmerings of what we can hope may be possible. Whoever you may be, I hope you will read it and find it speaks to you.'

– Prof. Cora Diamond, author of *The realistic spirit*

'Truth-telling is often hard because people don't like to hear bad news. But now our lives are on the line: if we refuse to face the difficult trade-offs that we'll have to make in order to prevent catastrophic climate change, then it's game over. Rupert Read's book on climate-truthfulness is filled with eloquent honesty about what's at stake, where we're currently headed, and what we can do. This is a vitally important book on the most crucial issue humanity has ever faced.'

– Richard Heinberg, Senior Fellow, Post Carbon Institute; author of *Power: Limits and prospects for human survival*

'Powerful and important, from a man who's been ahead of the climate curve for a long time.'

– Matthew Todd, author of *Straight Jacket* and essayist, including in *Letters to the Earth* and *This is not a drill: An Extinction Rebellion handbook*

'Rupert Read played a pivotal role in getting the BBC finally to stop seeking "balance" from climate-deniers and to start truth-telling on climate-reality. In this book, he reflects – with his trademark incisiveness and fearlessness – on the mission to confront the truth about where we as a civilisation have fallen short … and where to go from here. Insights drip from virtually every page. Just be warned: Don't read this book if you want to remain stuck in any kind of denial!'

– Chris Packham, BBC broadcaster

'Rupert Read is the rarest kind of philosopher, one who speaks from the heart. What he says, though, is rooted in science, so I think he is justified in referring to his book as rigorous truth-telling. He doesn't try to comfort us with false hopes but announces that it's game over for *this* civilisation. He invites us to imagine the one that might follow.'

– Prof. Clive Hamilton, author of *Defiant Earth: The fate of humans in the Anthropocene*

do you
want to
know the
TRUTH?

The surprising rewards of climate honesty

Rupert Read

Do you want to know the truth?
The surprising rewards of climate honesty

Published by the Simplicity Institute, Melbourne 2022
www.simplicityinstitute.org

ISBN: 978-0-6488405-5-8 (print)
ISBN: 978-0-6488405-6-5 (e-book)

I am aware, that many object to the severity of my language; but is there not cause for severity? I will be as harsh as truth, and as uncompromising as justice … I am in earnest – I will not equivocate – I will not excuse…

– William Lloyd Garrison, 1831

Contents

'Do you want to know the truth?'

So my sister was wanting to buy a pet rabbit. She goes to the man selling the rabbits, finds a bunny she really likes, moves to pet it a little, and then asks him: 'Was this rabbit handled much when it was young?' As anyone who knows pet rabbits will be aware, she asks this question because, if a rabbit is not handled when young, then it is harder for it to get used to humans later in life. Anyway, she waits for the man to answer, and he stares at her intently and then asks: 'Do you want to know the truth?'. At this, she pauses for a second, slightly dumbfounded, and then replies: 'Well, yes!'

Of course. It should go without saying that she wanted to know the truth. Because she wanted to know the answer to her question. What she wanted to know was the truth. That is, she wanted to know the actual answer to her question. Otherwise, she wouldn't have asked it.

So far, so obvious. What we need to try to understand then is what on earth is going on in the mind of the man who asked: 'Do you want to know the truth?' The answer to that must be something along the lines of: that he explicated something that normally remains implicit. For he was aware that sometimes, albeit bizarrely, it seems that people would much rather hear a comforting lie than an uncomfortable, inconvenient truth. The reality was that this rabbit had *not* been handled when it was young. Maybe, he figured, my sister would rather be told what she wanted – hoped – to hear.[1] Then, however, there would of course have been a big downside: she would have ended up with a rabbit who had not been handled, while labouring under the illusion that it had been. Not a happy situation to be in! (And reminiscent of the problematic contemporary habit of people prefacing certain remarks by saying, 'To be honest…', or, worse still, 'If I'm honest…', as though they'd rather tell a lie, – or even as though they *do* routinely lie when not marking their speech otherwise.)

We could apply this humble parable of the rabbit to 'the climate and ecological emergency' – only, here, the stakes are vastly higher, and the temptation to shy away from uncomfortable truths concomitantly that much greater. Of course, it means that the stakes of allowing oneself to rest in a condition of untruth are also much greater. Being under the illusion that a serene and smooth green transition is possible, or is even actually happening, might be good for one's temporary peace of mind. But living in that lie will end up facilitating such an unhappy situation that one can barely even imagine it. For we will then be deprived of the effect of the fire alarm, the warning shot across the bows. We will lose *response time* we simply can't afford to lose.

We are now starting to experience the disastrous consequences of most of us having failed thus far to ask the question of what the truth really is, however bitter it be. We are experiencing living in the age of consequences.

This book is about how it ought to go without saying that we want to know what the truth is. But more than that, it's about why it doesn't always go without saying: it's about our resistances of the will, which we must overcome. And more even than that, the following pages are about how, in the kingdom of the lie, and the empire of bullshit, the willingness to allow the truth in can be revolutionary.

This book centrally concerns how letting the truth in already is *being* revolutionary. How since the advent of Extinction Rebellion (XR) and of Greta Thunberg the world has changed, and, moreover, the call upon us – to tell and hear and live in truth – is an endless taskmaster.[2] As the book goes on, I explore the 'radical' *and* 'moderate' movements that are emerging from the wake of XR and Fridays For Future, which surpass them by applying even more strictly the game-changing injunction to tell the whole truth, including the uncomfortable bits. *Especially* the uncomfortable bits.

Finally, people have started to allow themselves to wake up and look up. This book – compiling and comprising accessible thinking (published and unpublished) of mine on this topic from these last few, revolutionary years – asks you a question. *Do you really want to know the truth; are you really willing to let it in, to be changed by it?* My hope is to demonstrate that the answer must, simply must, be: Yes.

One might hope that the mere fact of your having chosen to start reading this book already implies such a positive answer. But, as we shall see, the matter is not so simple. Fully facing up to the ecological 'emergency'[3] is harder than facing the facts about acquiring a pet bunny rabbit.

But, insofar as your answer is Yes, then we can breathe a cleaner air. We can then turn to each other, and begin to carry out the 'Great Work'[4] that we are called to.

Introduction
Dare to acknowledge
what you already know

I told a long-time, hard-core climate-activist colleague that I was writing a book called *Do You Want to Know the Truth?*. She responded with a slightly rueful and ironic laugh – then said, with a serious and slightly mournful undertone, 'No!'

This book is about that: We know we don't want to know the truth… *and* we know we need to know it.

In this book, I'm going to level with you. Do you want to be levelled with? You surely do. For only if you are levelled with are we on the same level, equals, rather than me thinking that I am superior to you, able to handle truths you allegedly cannot. And only if I level with you, am I really *on* the level.

These truths are completely general; obviously they are not specific to me (or to you). And yet, simple and crystalline though they are, they are not always present to us. They certainly were not always fully present to me. For most of my adult life, while priding myself in my personal life on my honesty, like so many before me (and since), I now recognise that I veered consistently just a little clear of this fulsome embrace of truthfulness in public and political life.

This Introduction will take the form of a short narrative of how I reached the point of experimenting with telling the whole truth, as I see and know it. That narrative sequentially introduces the main body of this book. This book's chapters fall one by one out of my journey into truth; a journey that many of us have been taking together in recent years – and many more of us have still been putting off.

My experiments with telling truths

I became an (often-'radical', often-'moderate') consistently committed green activist soon after moving to America to do a PhD at the start of the 1990s. The experience of the USA quickly radicalised me. Living in New Jersey, I was shocked at the urban sprawl, the vastness of pollution, the extreme economic division, the institutionalised (and yet disavowed) racism, the shallowness of so much life, and the lack of historical consciousness.

For a quarter of a century, there and in the UK, I fought a good fight, primarily in non-violent direct-action movements (EarthFirst!, radical animal rights, the nuclear disarmament organisation Trident Ploughshares) *and* the Green Party. During the early 21st century, my philosophical research increasingly turned to providing underpinnings for heavily critical assessments of the philosophy of possessive liberal individualism by which we are possessed. Especially in relation to the widespread, profoundly harmful sense of entitlement towards what (in a deadening, alienating turn of phrase) our civilisation typically calls 'the environment' (as opposed to nature, Earth, Gaia, etc.).

Then in late Spring 2015, all this suddenly changed for me. I was delivering Green Party leaflets one day in the ward where I lived, during the General Election campaign, and noticing the front gardens: manicured and weed-killered, or strewn with litter, dead fridges, cars, and so forth… And these words flashed into my head unbidden: '*This civilisation is finished*'. I stopped walking, thunderstruck. It was as if a daimon had spoken to me. Or a muse.

After being stuck in a state of shock for a couple of days, I did what intellectuals do: I started writing about it. I gradually wrote a piece called – you guessed it – '*This civilisation* is finished'. I was extremely hesitant about it. It was like nothing I'd ever written before. Compared to my previous writing, it seemed to drip with truth; the painful kind.

5

I gradually came to realise in the months after that four-word satori that, prior to that point, while I had thought I'd long been living with integrity, I hadn't actually been living in truth.[5] When those four words redounded suddenly through my head, it was a massive attack of truth. I came to realise then that I'd been talking the talk, but not really talking about (let alone walking) what I now dare to call 'climate breakdown'.[6] Which is but the most telling part of a more general ecological crisis. Which in turn is the product of a civilisational crisis.

I circulated the essay to some very-trusted intellectual friends and activist-colleagues. I relayed to them that I was hesitant to bring the new piece into the world, because I was worried I'd be attacked for 'giving up', and because I was worried I'd inadvertently encourage others to give up; the last thing I want. To a person, these colleagues and friends responded that they thought the piece quite simply the most important I'd ever written. Especially, in laying out a three-way schema of the choice we now face between transforming – butterfly-like – our civilisation into something new, on the one hand, or it being *terminated* for us, on the other; with that latter choice sub-dividing into a phoenix, a successor-civilisation(s), rising from the ashes of our failed civilisation on the one hand, and a more thoroughly dodo-like future for humanity on the other.

So, when one of these colleagues eventually urged me to publish the piece on his site, I finally, after some further hesitation, took the risk of publishing it;[7] though I took the precaution of doing so anonymously, something I'd never done before. Again, reaction was on balance very…well, *positive*. I moved to the next stage: I started giving the piece as a public talk, with great trepidation at first, still sorely afeared of being denounced or (worse) demoralising people. As a talk, '*This civilisation is finished*' came alive in a way that nothing I'd ever done before had. The feared attacks on me did not transpire (at least, not yet!). And most people who heard it seemed motivated and indeed energised rather than demoralised. It would seem that not only does speaking with radical honestly have the best chance of channeling the truth… it also *works*.

Of course, that realisation is hardly mine alone! And indeed it was central, for instance, to the strategy XR employed. XR's first demand, 'Tell the truth', is foundational for all the rest.

So far in this Introduction, I have given you a glimpse of my story, my experiments with telling truths. But this is – of course – one story among so many along broadly similar lines.

There is in fact a long tradition of people warning of potential climate catastrophe, some of them doing so on the basis of rigorous scientific analysis, others doing so in more *imaginative* ways (notably in Science Fiction). I place myself in a large and ever-growing group of like-minded people who have had much the same revelation as I describe above (shortly after or before me). Within the movement that I have long been part of, there have been certain trends on which I have been building in my recent life and work. I now want to invite more people into this 'forum', to involve them (you) in ongoing discussions – and (responsive) actions. That many of us – from Green House to Jem Bendell, from Mark Lynas to Joanna Macy, and so on – have been going through analogous difficult processes for some time is itself a fact that makes things a little bit easier. It doesn't eliminate how difficult this acknowledgement of a very important and painful truth can be; but *when we know that we are in good company, we no longer feel so alone.* And *therein* lies support, encouragement, even potentially enthusiasm.

What is in this book

The first piece in this book, published here under the retrospective title 'Why I had to tell my students I fear for them', obviously comes straight out of the stable that I've described in the section above. It was my first attempt to tell the nub of the whole truth to the younger generation, at the university where I teach. First year students came to me in numbers after it, saying things like, 'This feels like the first time in my life that someone in a position of authority has levelled with me' and 'It's almost welcome to finally hear what you said spoken aloud'. They felt freed, and strangely buoyed, even relieved in a certain sense.

In time the attacks did come – though mostly from real opponents, not so much from 'my own side' (an exception being the topic of Chapter 9). They came mostly after I had given 'This civilisation is finished' as a public lecture at Cambridge University[8] and it had gone viral. Yet, despite the attacks, a number of XR 'arrestables' in 2019 told me the talk had inspired them to come onto the streets and sit down or 'lock on'. There is no greater compliment that I could have wished for.

One reason I believe that 'This civilisation is finished' had such a great impact, way more than interventions and talks I'd given before, is that it began with a stark and humble admission of failure, to date. Addressing the university students in the audience, I said these words: 'Your so-called leaders have failed you. Your teachers, despite the best of their intentions, have failed you. Your parents surely love you; but they too have failed you. And I have failed you.' The levelling effect of this truth made possible the resonance that followed.

By this time I had helped launch Extinction Rebellion;[9] the most meaningful part of my life to date was underway. For I'd truly found my life's purpose. I'd found that, like others in XR and the inspirational Greta Thunberg, I could speak truth unadorned, with raw emotion, in front of crowds or (more significant still, perhaps) in the belly of the machine, and that this authenticity could move even hardened politicians and civil servants and businesspeople and journalists. I'd found that the raw truth could cut through where decades of campaigning had failed to. When we allow ourselves to face and voice our fears, our griefs, our anger, our love, when we get real about the ecological horror-story, and about our having passed out of the climate safe-zone, then so much more becomes possible; and actual.

When I was first giving talks on why this civilisation is finished, I'd had an instinct, a difficult knowing, but not really a plan. XR brought to the table a plan: tell the truth without reservation, break free of 'toxic positivity', undertake mass sustained non-violent direct action (NVDA), and force a game-changing national conversation. Then get to speak this truth with power directly, and even power will shift, following the citizenry.

In April 2019, especially in the UK, the essence of the plan worked. After that time, in some key respects, XR gradually started to lose its way,[10] and the machine gradually pushed back cleverly (I turn to the implications of *these* points for the future of climate movements in the Conclusion to this book). But for a glorious moment XR raised climate consciousness and conscience in a way that had a lasting impact upon this country and the world. For power conceded something to each of XR's demands. On Demand 1, 'Tell The Truth', Parliament declared a Climate and Environment Emergency (albeit only a symbolic one) shortly after we met with Environment Minister Michael Gove and other government ministers at the end of the April 2019 Rebellion. Demand 2, 'Act Now (to go Carbon Net Zero)', was unexpectedly legislated for that summer in the UK (albeit by 2050, not 2025!). Demand 3, for Citizens Assemblies to chart the way forward, saw six Commons Select Committees create a Climate Citizens Assembly beginning that summer (albeit one without real teeth, and with various unfortunate limitations in its remit). Moreover, what XR achieved together in 2018–19 was an end-game for hard climate denialism. Except in some redoubts in the USA and Australia, it mostly gave up (and moved on to climate delayism).

Chapters 2 and 3 come from the effort I joined 'Writers Rebel' in in 2020 to get the lobby groups (aka 'thinktanks') based at Tufton Street in the heart of Westminster exposed to proper scrutiny. These two pieces chart a particular thread of the XR-inspired struggle to get the whole truth told: in this case, to shed a light on the remains of the nefarious dark-money-backed climate denialism that still tries to find a hold within our politics, even after the initial victory in public consciousness of XR and Fridays For Future. It is an intriguing fact that it was very soon after we shone a light on the nefarious think tanks at 55 Tufton Street that the Global Warming Policy Foundation rebranded itself as 'Net Zero Watch'.[11] This is the move from climate denial (pretending as they did that global over-heat did not exist) to climate delay (pretending as they now do merely to scrutinise the policies designed to bring us toward net zero).

Chapter 4, entitled 'Act now *because* it's too late', takes us deeper into what then, as I started to move beyond XR, was emerging into focus for me: the need to radicalise the demand for truth still further.[12] To come clean (something which XR has sometimes shied away from doing,[13] with the slogan of that Rebellion, 'Act now because it's too late', being something of a glorious *exception*), that the tragic truth was that our demands were not going to be acceded to in full, nothing like; and that therefore we had to start to pivot towards accepting and handling the consequences. (Especially, the need to take *adaptation* seriously; on which, see especially the Conclusion to this book.)

The two chapters on the new Greens Climate Activist Network I've co-founded, chapters 5 and 6, take us deeper into this territory – the territory of applying the power of the powerless. This is the paradoxical realm where one's greatest power can emerge from admitting inefficaciousness. The second of these pieces already leans in toward the vein I've just been mining: for in it I recognise a respect in which the power of truth can turn out to be limited.

It wouldn't be truthful, to avoid this. The truth includes the fact that truthfulness is not a silver bullet; it doesn't magically get everything done.

Of course, the potential beauty of *this* vein of 'meta-honesty' – being honest about the limited of the efficacy of honesty alone – is that by way of it we may be able to re-activate the power of the powerless. By coming clean about tragic limits *of the power of truthfulness* to power us, we may be able to relaunch that very power. For one is then leaning in again to truth, even when one would much rather report glorious take-up, resonance, success. The very fact that sometimes one's audience is not yet ready to resonate with one's message – such that we are going to suffer yet more frustrating and deleterious delay – can *itself* be something that, by resonating with those who can then see what this sadly or horrifyingly means, repowers us![14]

The two chapters on COP26, 7 and 8, focus in on the passing of the 1.5°C 'safe' target, a lynchpin when it comes to the epochal response we can potentially leverage from speaking (and living in) truth. The endless 'Yes we can, it's only five minutes to midnight!' breathlessness is no longer working. Did it ever, really? I propose that only by admitting it's 'five past midnight' do we have a chance, through 'reloading' on truth, of recharging (and greatly growing) the broadest possible movement for the next stage of the journey.

I emphasise in this book that such a reloading involves not only facing the darkness of the truth about the climate itself but also the related truth about the historical failure, on balance, of the environmental movement and world scientific community, in this most vital of fields. We did not succeed in influencing action and policy in anything like a sufficient way,[15] and as a result our warnings have in practice largely gone ignored, even as the situation has worsened. Ignoring 50 years or more of warnings was always bound to have serious consequences and is now exerting a huge cost. That cost cannot be negotiated away. You can't bargain with the atmosphere.

This heaviest of costs, the vast legacy of delay and inefficacy, is difficult to accept even for many of us who have spent our lives giving out those warnings. In fact, *especially* for them/us! That's why I keep returning to (seek to) address especially scientists / 'activists' / Greens etc., in this book. The book is for everyone, insofar as we *all* need to face up to climate reality and to disclose the truths that we are privy to (I mean here everything from being authentic about our loves and fears about the crisis to blowing the whistle in ways that at this time insurers, government officials, fossil fuel employees and many more are called to do). But facing up to our own failure to face up to climate reality is particularly *difficult* for those of us who have invested ourselves in the project of seeking to get sufficient action on climate and ecology. It is desperately hard for us in particular to admit that the clock has passed midnight. And to accept our own complicity in what has gone wrong. To accept the need for a change of story, of approach.

So what I'm finding so far, perhaps not surprisingly, is quite a lot of resistance to this new 'five past midnight' narrative that, along with

Marc Lopatin and others, I'm setting out, and quite a lot of clinging on tight to the 1.5 delusion; *especially*, close to home (e.g., among climate scientists, the youth climate strikers, the Green Party, etc.). It turns out that acknowledging at a general level that *this* civilisation is surely finished may actually be easier than getting really specific about our having exited the 'safe' zone.[16] Perhaps because when it comes to it there is an unconscious clinging to any slight wiggle-room, any chance of avoiding the brutal impact of facing up to the failure to keep us safe of the Paris Accord on climate. That has been my experience recently: that there is a widespread tendency to grasp for straws. And that this tendency is persistent among scientists and activists who one suspects know better.

Some of this resistance takes the form of stating that we yet cannot know with 100% certainty that 1.5°C is gone. This is technically true, but doesn't take into account this crucial, precautionary point: Taking the insistence that we needed to stay below 1.5 to be safe at face-value, we're already not safe now because to be confident beyond reasonable doubt of staying below 1.5, we'd have to go net zero carbon world-wide by about...2022.[17]

If you are not confident you are going to be able to stay safe, *you are not safe.* It's not just that you do not *feel* safe (though that is hardly unimportant), it's that you are *not* safe epistemologically speaking (i.e., you are not in a space of safety if you can't reliably *take* yourself to be safe). The carbon budget for staying *safe* – for not *potentially* entering the above-1.5 danger zone – is gone already. We may well exceed 1.5 degrees at least temporarily within the next few years. Moreover, scientists say that we have until about 2032 to go zero carbon for a 50% chance of staying below 1.5, and until just 2030 for a 67% chance of staying below 1.5. For a high 90s percentage confidence – not far below 100%, i.e., perhaps beyond reasonable doubt – of staying below 1.5? It is striking that that question barely enters public debate, but roughly it would require us to go zero-carbon by, at the latest, the end of this year, the year of writing.[18] (Of course, you may be reading it in 2023, or 2024, in which case it is very much in the rear-view mirror.)

The *2025* target was utterly eye-watering when XR first flew the flag for it in 2018. As this book goes to print, we're most of the way through 2022. We're completely out of time. We're out of wiggle-room. We're out of the safe zone. The longer we pretend otherwise, the more we're wasting time we don't have. In sum, beyond reasonable doubt, the 1.5°C target is already lost. *Admitting this at once and drawing the consequences could just be the most powerful thing we ever do.*

Chapter 9, 'An open letter to Michael Mann' is an endeavour to do exactly this in response to one of the world's most famous climate scientists, who is inadvertently blocking the possibility of climate-truth-telling. In an exchange with Mann that I had on BBC national radio at the end of COP26 (it was supposed to be a straight debate, but in the end Mann refused to engage me in direct debate), he demonstrated what I see as a paradigm example of climate Pollyannaism, a near-complete refusal to face the reality of the failure of the COP process to keep us safe. But, while Mann has attacked and defamed me (and XR, and many more besides), my response is an attempt to call him in, rather than calling him out.

Chapter 10, 'What is the main obstacle to the truth about climate breakdown being told' brings together and deepens the account offered in earlier chapters in this book; it is the most substantive chapter of the lot. In it, I urge us to have faith that living in truth is not for an elite, but for many of us – *if* we are to have a chance of getting through what is approaching in a condition that's closer to 'butterfly' (or at least 'phoenix') than 'dodo'. There is something recklessly arrogant about the assumption that the masses cannot take the truth that scientists are contemplating and struggling with. Rather, what is needed is to deliver it plain, but to deliver it with love, with humanity, in supportive contexts. And I've already noted that my own experience has been that ordinary people, especially those primed to learn (such as university students), are surprisingly keen to hear such unadorned truth.

We need to *deliver* the truth, like a baby. It needs to be allowed to emerge into the light. *And* we need to be clear that it mostly isn't quite about 'delivering' anything new. Because many people already *know* in their bones; they sense where we are at. They hear the outlines of the science; they witness the inefficacious response; they sense the vulnerability of the fragile civilisation we share.

That is part of the reason for the astonishingly high percentages who, on the rare occasions they get asked, will confess that they believe collapse to be likely. Despite – or partly *because* of? – such an outcome being still largely completely taboo in 'respectable' public discourse: I mean that, even now, detailed contemplation of potential climate-induced societal collapse and of inevitable civilisational transformation is astonishingly, vanishingly rare, in the media, academia, or politics.

'This is not an emergency', Chapter 11, sets out another key, related aspect of our painful, needful progress: urging the difficult task of recognising that this that we are in is a worse-than-emergency, a more-than-emergency. Calling it an 'emergency', far from overplaying our hand, runs the double-hazard of both over-*stressing* us (and our audience) and *underplaying* the true enormity and insolubility of our predicament. Our house is on fire; and yet this metaphor misleads, in that it encourages us to fantasise that we can put the fire out within our lifetimes, or run out of the house. Instead, let us play a longer, deeper game. Accepting the tragic implication that there simply is going to be much suffering and death, oceans of it. We are going to have to bear 'unbearable' losses. This is what the Green Party and even XR – which together fostered the inspiring, successful drive for widespread declarations of 'Climate emergency!' – have tended not to be willing to acknowledge.

Consider the following quote, which is a typical recent example of 'stubborn optimism', from *The Guardian*[19] newspaper:

> 'If you're going to sound the fire alarm, you've got to show people where the exits are…and there aren't enough narratives showing those exits.'

This is a call for 'more optimism', 'more solutions'. XR and Greta Thunberg sounded the fire alarm. Now we need to be shown the fire exits. Sounds intuitive. Sounds good. Right? Wrong.[20] Here's the thing that's unfortunate about that metaphor… There *aren't* any 'exits' unless you fantasise the route that Jeff Bezos, Elon Musk and others evidently want to take: the impossible, deadly dream of exiting Earth altogether. There are only better and worse ways of staying put – turning *toward* the fire – and fighting it. We desperately want exits, reprieves, silver bullets. That's actually part of the problem – the much-more-than-problem – that defines our time.

This leads into Chapter 12, on charting the story beyond cruel optimism.[21] Extreme Pollyannaism, which is still widespread, calls out any mere hint of stating the full direness of our predicament – let alone of the possibility of a collapse – as a kind of giving up. Chapter 12 seeks to show how this stubborn toxic positivity is actually a way of prolonging the agony, the interregnum before we turn with full determination to harm-reduction, strategic adaptation, and climate justice. For there is no climate justice in pretending that we are going to keep the Global South – or anywhere – from the consequences of breaching the 1.5 degrees 'safe' limit; on the contrary. The massive betrayal that is the result of long prevarication must be confronted if we are to get serious at last about helping the Global South transformatively adapt and indeed bear the loss and damage that is coming – if it is not here already. We are *in* what Churchill called 'the age of consequences'. And some of us are more in it than others; they need our help.

Chapter 13 takes stock of how the hopes that COVID-19 or Ukraine would be wake-up calls the world needed to 'go green' have fallen far short. For the 'meta-crisis' of our system is too profound to be entirely remedied by the opportunity falling into our laps by way of such specific crises (though they *are* wake-up calls, available opportunities, thankfully taken by some of us, for the kind of moments of disturbing and even revelatory clarity to which I referred earlier). We will not make real progress until we are ready to absorb this lesson, which once again has centrally to do with story (plus of course with vested interests and raw power!).[22] This chapter seeks to help change the hegemonic cultural story (of 'progress', of meeting 'needs' by way of markets, of petro-fuelled 'freedom') by seeing the whole nexus of factors around the terrible attack on Ukraine and its consequences as joined-up: as an expression of the failed operating system of this civilisation. Thus it will require a much deeper reset to move us onto a different, post-carbon footing; a reset which cannot be seen as *likely* to come this side of collapse.

But a reset cannot quite be ruled out. For ruling it out – embracing a form of doomism – is just another default-setting of the current recipe for passivity. Doomism, just as much as Pollyannaism, is a way of avoiding the reckoning, and of avoiding our full agency. We tend to *want* to avoid our agency because, if we were to embrace its fullness, we would be in the ultimate position of pain: knowing it possible that we could change course and that we *ourselves* could potentially be significantly instrumental in that course-change, while knowing how improbable it is that very much of a course-change will in fact successfully be executed.

We want a reprieve. We want to be excused from having to act with determination, together. We want to be able to give up, or to outsource the responsibility to act adequately to others. But *it is not possible.*

Call this realisation 'stubborn realism'.

My 2020 book *Extinction Rebellion: Insights from the Inside* ended with a chapter entitled 'Now is the time: Or else our hopes start to fade'. Well, the world failed on balance to respond adequately to the spark of XR, or to the opportunity presented by the crisis that was the advent of the coronavirus, or to the opportunity by the crisis that is the invasion of Ukraine. So *some* of our hopes *have* to fade. That is the honesty that is required of us, an honesty that even XR has struggled to manifest; *only if we* give up hopes that are no longer realistic *can we seriously and energetically pursue* those hopes that remain live. That's what the chapters situated towards the end of this book seek to show.

The Conclusion re-engages the considerations opened up here in this Introduction and explored throughout the book. I consider what lessons to draw from the last several years' worth of experiments with climate-truth-telling, in terms of mobilisation and action. For most of this book I don't offer much by way of practical advice or guidance on how to *organise* on the basis of telling the truth. I *do* turn to that question, explicitly, in the Conclusion: I lay out there how, if what I say in the body of the book resonates with you, you might choose to join me and others in deepening your engagement in a truth-based movement(s) or form of practice that can change the world, profoundly, in the kind of way it desperately needs changing. And I lay out why the journey that I personally have been on, documented in this book, might be helpful to others. My view now, set out in the Conclusion, is that a fundamentally truth-based agenda will lead nearly everyone to step up what they do, but that that step will in most cases not be to the model of radical flanks, but rather into the power of a potentially much larger and in an important sense more 'positive' movement, a mass 'moderate' flank. This is surely on balance an encouraging thought. Albeit for some of us veterans an uncomfortable one.

And so I return finally, too, in the Conclusion to explicit consideration of the question opened up in the Preface, above: Do you want to know the truth? Really? I return to the anecdote of my sister's encounter with the man selling rabbits – and draw from it, perhaps-surprisingly, a hopeful conclusion…

Sapere Aude!

Before we embark into the body of the book, let me deal with a potential objection to my endeavour here. Am I (arrogantly?) assuming that I *know* the truth, unlike benighted opponents?

There are two parts to the answer to this question.

The first part is to say: to some extent *yes*. The point of view that I and folk like me have been pursuing doggedly for a while now is, tragically, being vindicated: in the spinning out of control of the world's weather, in the profound inadequacy of the system's response thereto, in a still-widespread lack of understanding of ecology and of the insanity of the ideology of growthism, and much more besides. Consider the recent successful BBC TV series 'Big oil vs the world', which delivers in crunching, awful detail how big oil companies knew the climatic implications of their industry, and how much of the world allowed themselves to be hoodwinked. The series could equally have been called, 'Big oil vs the truth'.

We told you so. The real reason people don't like to hear 'We told you so' is that it exposes their own failure to listen. So they try to shoot the messenger, focusing on the alleged arrogance of those who had the vision or the simple evidence-based-willingness to live in truth; rather than having the humility to let themselves focus on their own shortcomings, and learning lessons.

An important qualification: In this book, I do not present a *comprehensive scholarly* case for the truth of the situation as I have just indicated it. I do link to plenty of sources. But rather than weighing this book down with hundreds of academic references to evidence certain of my claims, I refer the reader to my *previous* work; *plus* I've collated a number of pivotal scholarly sources in an annotated 'fundamental bibliography' at the end of this book. Those who would like the detail are encouraged to consult those reports, essays, and books. In other words, *this* book does not present a scholarly case for our being in a condition of ecological breakdown.[23] Rather, it is about exploring the potential of speaking with radical honesty about the scholarly case *that already exists*.

Nor does this relatively concise book explore in detail the 'solutions' that exist to our predicament. For instance, there are no detailed discussions of how to end GDP-growth (or what a post-growth society will look like), or how to relocalise our riskily-over-extended globalised supply chains; I've discussed these matters at some length elsewhere, as of course have others. Rather, this book is about the potential of speaking in full truthfulness to liberate and mobilise us into full action *on such fronts*. My case is that without a deeper dive into the power of truth, we are never going to get the sensible bold action that is *vital* in these domains.

Now, for the second part of the answer to the question that was raised above, which balances the first and is equally important. To some significant extent the answer is *no*. Obviously, I don't know the whole truth. Not even 'we', combined – those who warned about what was coming, what is now here, if not yet equally distributed – know the whole truth. To say this is simply to acknowledge what is often called 'human finitude'. It is to embrace an absolutely essential humility: one which our civilisation, tellingly, has been poor at embracing. I am speaking of the spirit of open-ended inquiry, rather than of premature certainty, or importunate knowingness.

My work for a good number of years now has been centrally concerned with and firmly based on the Precautionary Principle. I have worked with Nassim Taleb and others to set out how we must live in a world that we will never 'fully' understand. I systematically oppose the scientism and plain hubris of those who think we know what the future will hold (including, crucially, as explained above, those who claim to 'know' that we are doomed *or* to 'know' that we will be fine/that our civilisation will survive/prosper). My work in the philosophy of science, which until relatively recently was the main area in which I published academically, has been *devoted* to setting out the risks science runs of over-stating its certainties.

We have no choice but to live in uncertainty. Only such living is living in truth, beyond the false complacent pseudo-'certainties' of doomerism on the one hand and of imagined outsourced salvation on the other.

My philosophical attitude is that we need to *seek* (to know) truth; that we must counterpose a permanent orientation of truthfulness to the inanities and insanities of (the fantasy of) 'post-truth'. This orientation begins with key cases such as the media, which we must require not to just give us 'He said, she said; there's two sides to every story' stories of 'balance', but to be willing to be clear about which stories are true and which aren't! But crucially, and to stay with the illustrative case of the media, such an orientation deepens with the utter importance of a spirit of *investigation* (as per 'investigative journalism'). It isn't enough to be truthful if one fails to seek to *find out* more.

Truthfulness is a task, a struggle we engage in. A struggle with (the forces of) untruth, and with ourselves. We should keep searching; science that actually is science (rather than engineering or technological application – or dogma) has, always, an open frontier. Moreover, 'environmentalism' in the past has occasionally made substantive missteps, when it has pretended to know more than was knowable: e.g., certain claims about timescales for metals running out.

The truth will set you free – provided it is *pursued* in the fashion outlined right here, and not complacently *assumed*. The voice I aim at manifesting in this book might in this regard perhaps be described as 'prophetic'. That does *not* mean 'predictive'. I don't make predictions, still less express confidence about things one cannot be certain of. What I do (here and elsewhere) is:

To pose potential scenarios, between which we have some agency.

To talk about what is intrinsically good to do *no matter what* happens (e.g., to live in truth): so, 'no-regrets' policies.

And…

To dive into the instrumental value of truthfulness: the way that it works, the uses it has, which have been neglected out of misplaced fear of the consequences of truth-telling.

Moreover, there is much that we already know that we may not know/ acknowledge that we know (this is what Donald Rumsfeld, in his helpful well-known typology, left out: the paradoxical but profoundly pertinent *unknown knowns*). There's much of this kind that we know if we dare to face it. Here is a new meaning to the phrase that the Enlightenment made famous, 'Sapere Aude'! 'Dare to know'! Above all, I invite you into that spirit (thus inflected!) in this book: dare to let yourself acknowledge what your heart and gut already at-least-half-know.

Dare to know the terrible truth about climate and ecological breakdown. Dare too to tell it – and the truth *will* set you free. Living in truth has within it a power beyond our imaginings. In *Extinction Rebellion: Insights from the inside* I argued that the radical power of Extinction Rebellion's first and most important demand, Tell The Truth, had not yet been taken seriously enough *even by XR itself*. We have to take that demand more seriously.

This book is *an invitation to truthfulness*; to what Vaclav Havel called 'living in truth'. What we have seen of it from XR and Greta is but the start, the merest (magnificent) *glimmerings*. This mighty power of love, of truth-force, is, I firmly believe, going to flower in the most astonishing and world-moving ways, in the immensely challenging times of which we are as yet only on the cusp.

So: are you ready to be levelled with? *Do you* want to know the truth?

Chapter 1
Why I had to tell my students that I fear for them

This is a lightly edited version of my 'welcoming address' to first-year students at the University of East Anglia, at the beginning of the autumn semester of 2016. The title is retrospective; it refers the reader to the mood and orientation which came upon me when thinking about why I had taken the hard decision to give this talk at all.

The reaction to the talk was a huge encouragement. An intense Q&A followed, featuring especial interest in the idea of 'Guardians for future generations'; and then a queue of students lined up to speak with me, keen to know more and to confirm to me how welcome it was to hear a teacher actually telling the bitter truth about where we are at.

My giving of the talk, over which I had agonised, felt vindicated, and from this moment on I determined to do the same at every opportunity.

First published on Medium[24] *(and on* Eastminster*), 28 January 2017.*

Welcome to University! Welcome to perhaps the most amazing opportunity of your lives. Welcome to the astonishing gift that is three years in which to think and learn, three years of the life of the mind.

Though I have to tell you… I don't envy you.

The reason I don't envy you is because, as I look around the room, with very few exceptions, most of you are significantly younger than me. And I think there is a very real possibility that the latter part of the lives of most of you in this room is going to be grim or non-existent. I'm sorry to have to say it. I'm sorry to have to level with you.

I'm fearful for you.

I hear a little nervous laughter now. I think that's because people just don't usually say this kind of thing. There's an extreme taboo around it – and that's partly what I want to talk about.

As you may know, here at the University of East Anglia we have one of the world's leading environmental science departments – especially on climate science – and what they tell us is extremely grim. If you read their academic papers or popular versions of their papers, they suggest that unless our civilisation manages to turn itself around in quite a dramatic way in quite a short space of time (and there is no real sign as yet of this happening), then the future – well within your lifetimes – is going to be unrecognisable, and unrecognisably worse.

Also, it's actually even worse than that because if you manage to talk to them 'off the record', if you get them in the bar or something, then they will say things like, 'Well, you know, actually in our papers we're pretty conservative; we only publish what we can *prove*'; or, 'It could be a lot *worse* than that.' I actually think that you in this room here today should be very angry with the generation that's older than you and the generation before that. Because there's been what I would call a 'festival' of recklessness or a 'carnival' of short-termism that has characterised the last generations. It leaves *you* in a very parlous position; and it's all too easy, I'm afraid, for such festivals to turn into funerals.

So what are we to do about this?

I want to suggest two things we need to do by way of thinking about this. And think about it we must. This is nothing if not a moment for profound reflection.

One is that we address it philosophically. What does it mean to address it philosophically? It means that we try to *imagine* (for example) how different the future will be if we get to the point – which we may well get to within your lifetimes – where it becomes clear and unavoidable that for the foreseeable future *each generation is likely to have a materially worse life than the generation that came before it.* Even if we do our very best and have some real success and some luck along the way.

If that happens it's going to be – to force – an enormous change in human consciousness, because for so long we thought that what life is essentially about is having a good time and bequeathing a *better* life to the next generation. It's going to be an enormous psychological, philosophical value challenge if we have to give that ambition up; if we have to give up the prejudice of 'progress'. It requires deep reflection, and courage, to even address this likelihood; to think about how we will reconcile ourselves to decline.

I'm not talking merely about a reduction in GDP. That's no great hardship in and of itself. I'm talking about what might turn out to be an ongoing reduction in actual quality of life, however well we organise ourselves. Because it is possible that the damage to our climate and to nature that we are letting rip – that collectively we are *driving* – may prove too severe to compensate for by smart self-organisation.

Secondly, I think we need to think about all this in terms of the very difficulty we have in thinking about it! I suspect this is symbolised by the slightly nervous titters of laughter which went up as I started speaking and confessed to something that I bet virtually no one has confessed to you before: my lack of envy for you, my fear for you, my shame before you, in the face of how badly you've been let down.

Why is it that we find it so difficult to face this horrific possibility, which may soon become a reality? I think one reason is the notorious frog-in-boiling-water syndrome, which many of you are probably aware of. If you put a frog in warm water and you gradually heat up the water, eventually you have boiled frog. The question, of course, is why didn't the frog jump out when the water started getting really hot? The answer that is standardly given is: because the temperature goes up so gradually that it barely gets noticed – and that is precisely the situation that we are in as a species.

Now here I want to tell you something hopeful. It's not true. Most frogs actually *do* jump out. You turn up the temperature enough, your average frog will jump out. I think we should take some hope from that. If frogs are smart enough to sort this out, then surely we should be. A great applied philosopher, Karl Marx, once said that human beings only set themselves such problems as they can solve, and I bet he's right. Only, I think the problem that I'm talking about here is a very, very difficult one to solve, so it's going to require a lot of work. It's going to require a lot of intellectual effort for starters.

Actually, it isn't a *problem* as such at all. It's something far bigger and deeper than that, for it will require a whole paradigm shift to tackle it.

So, for starters: am I in despair? Well, no; as I say, if frogs can do it then so surely can we. Let's show that in this respect, at least, Marx was right.

So that's why I've been thinking about ways in which we might start to change this culture of incredible recklessness and short-termism that we find ourselves in. This culture that is committed to serious risks of complete civilisational breakdown within the 21st century and thus within the lifetimes of many of you in this room. I want to share with you, quickly, two ideas that I've been working on, along with others, for how we might seek to make that change; for how we might become wise frogs.

The first idea is called the Precautionary Principle.

This principle is at the heart of the needed paradigm shift, the big change of approach that we need if we are to make it through what is coming. What the Precautionary Principle basically says is: better to act early, with precaution, than too late with potentially catastrophic consequences. In particular, as we elaborate on in a paper I'm writing along with Nassim Taleb,[25] where there is a risk of serious, potentially catastrophic or irreversible harm then you don't need to wait for all the evidence, you don't need to wait for 'full' scientific proof, before acting to forestall that harm; for where there is such a risk, that in itself mandates finding another route. For it is *irresponsible* under such circumstances to wait around for all the evidence. What is needed is *action* to change what is happening, not merely passive *observance* of unfolding disasters.

What then does such precaution mean in concrete terms? Well, for example, with regard to climate, what it would mean is that rather than having to prove categorically that the climate scientists are right and that their models can be 100% relied upon, we should take massive precautious action now. For their models suggest that if we continue on a business-as-usual path, we could have several degrees of global over-heating by the end of the century. This might not sound so bad but we have only had a one degree increase so far and yet we've already had the massive floods here a few years ago, we've already had the kinds of catastrophes that are regularly visited now on countries like Bangladesh and Australia, we're already seeing the coral reefs dying: when you understand how exponentially worse several degrees of over-heat and of climate chaos would be than this, and when you realise that for every degree of over-heat on average across the planet there is more than twice that on land and four times that in the Arctic... when you realise all this, then you know that business-as-usual or anything like it actually is an epically appalling proposition in relation to climate.

What the Precautionary Principle would say is that it would be reckless to await scientific proof before taking action, because in the interregnum we would potentially be allowing the entire human future to be destroyed or at least decimated. If the Precautionary Principle were to become a guiding principle of our societies – if we were to act wisely, ahead of certainty, to reduce our exposure to disaster – well then, the world might start to look very different, and the prognosis might look very different.

The second idea is institutionally entrenching care for the future. My idea is to establish guardians for future generations.[26] Let me explain. We seem to have a problem in that we are prone, especially nowadays, to the kind of recklessness and short-termism that I've already mentioned. This is symbolised, for example, by us chucking more and more greenhouse gases up into the atmosphere as if there's no tomorrow – which might well be the case eventually, unfortunately, if we carry on with the chucking. We are stuck in a form of short-termism that our normal modes of governance and government aren't good at getting us out of, to put it mildly. Politicians famously have relatively short time horizons; it's very difficult for them to think further than the next election. In fact, in many cases it's very difficult for them to think further than the next news cycle – which nowadays have shrunk to about 24 hours.

So – and here's my proposal – what if we were to have an institutional change which would make it possible and indeed necessary for people to think in the long term? My thought experiment is this: What if future generations – what if your children and their children – were here with us now? What would these generations tell us to do? What would they tell us not to do or to *stop* doing now?

Of course, until one of our colleagues in physics invents a time-travel machine, this is going to be impossible to realise in any straightforward sense. But what if we could create an institution that acted as a kind of proxy that somehow represented future generations? That's the nub of my idea, which is to suggest that as well as having our ordinary houses of parliament, there should be something like a third house which sits above them. This new house would have in it *representatives* of future generations who would be empowered to strike down any laws, including the government's budget, insofar as those laws recklessly endangered future generations by, for example, committing us to further climate-dangerous greenhouse gas emissions on a large scale.

Who should those representatives be? Who *are* the guardians of future generations? Plato, the great ancient philosopher, said that our guardians should be philosophers, which I'll confess to you is not an unappealing idea for someone in my profession… But I think it's an idea which is not very well suited to our rightly democratic sensibilities and time. So, my suggestion in developing this proposal of guardians of future generations is that the guardians should be each and any one of us, by which I mean they should be a random selection of the population who would be given this awesome responsibility of seeking to represent the future. You could think of them as a kind of super-jury. We give juries an awesome responsibility to stand in for the rest of us in judging those accused of wrongdoing. The guardians for future generations should be a super-jury representing our descendants, and would be placed in the same kind of position of awesome responsibility. Again, they could and, I think, should, be drawn democratically from each and any one of us.

These guardians would then embody us, and at the same time they would embody the future – they would embody our hope and intention to save ourselves, to save the world for those to come after us.[27]

So those are my two suggestions – a bold application of the Precautionary Principle and the establishment of Guardians of the Future. I don't know if they'll work, I don't know if they'll be enough. But one thing I do know: we need creative thinking and we need some radical answers; otherwise we're going to be in the situation which I started out by describing, where, in five or ten years' time I'm up here again feeling even less envious of those in the audience, and even more fearful for them.

I don't want it to be like that. I would like to be envious of you in every way, as you start this incredible adventure of your university education. I think there's nothing worse for human beings than the thought that they might be bequeathing to their descendants a worse world than the world they currently have.

So: welcome to university. I hope you are up to the challenges that await you. Be engaged; be bold; be creative. You will need to be.

Thank you.

Chapter 2
'We *are* power'

Speech to rebels and writers outside 55 Tufton Street

This speech was given, alongside XR co-founder Clare Farrell and Writers Rebel founder Jessica Townsend, on 7 September 2020, shortly before we undertook 'criminal damage' at 55 Tufton Street, Westminster as part of an Extinction Rebellion. (My part in this direct action consisted in pouring fake blood over the steps into the building) 55 Tufton Street is the offices of several secretive climate-catastrophic lobby groups (aka 'thinktanks'), most notably, the Global Warming Policy Foundation (since rebranded as Net Zero Watch).

The aim of our speeches and in the non-violent direct action that followed was to shed a light on the dark money that funds the nefarious activities of the GWPF and others, and to show to the world the truthless but sadly not toothless power that they wield. The nexus of lobby groups based in and around Tufton Street has been shown to wield real power in relation to Government.

But people-power, too, is real. And what we did on the day that this speech was given did indeed contribute to bringing about the shedding of some light, as Chapter 3 will help show…

The power behind state power is represented here, behind me, at 55 Tufton Street.

But I'm here to tell you: there's another power. A greater power. It's the power of truth. It's the power of numbers. It's the power of authenticity and determination.

We are the power.

We make that power.

You make that power

You are that power.

You

…*Are*

…Power.

Extinction?!

[Crowd] Rebellion!

Extinction?!

[Crowd] Rebellion!

Extinction?!

[Crowd] Rebellion!

Oh yes, my friends: always remember that you are power.

But let's take a moment, this moment, to remind ourselves why we're here.

As I speak to you this evening, parts of Pakistan and China are underwater. We are in a long and potentially terminal 'climate emergency'. And let's remind ourselves of the other half of the equation: habitat destruction. One thing about habitat destruction: it's undeniable. When they eradicate a football pitch of rainforest, and then another one, and then another one, and then another one, no one can really pretend that it isn't happening. That's why this lot don't talk about that so much. The climate denialists want to talk about climate and place those tiny seeds of doubt in people's minds. But there's nothing they can say on habitat destruction. They don't talk about it so much; and we should probably talk about it a great deal more. And we should talk about how our out-of-control economic system is what's destroying those habitats.

We're here because they're here. Because there is blood on their hands, just as surely as on Johnson's or on Shell's or on Exxon's. They like to hide from public scrutiny. We're here to shine the light of truth upon them. Just as they have responsibility for the pollution of the world's waters, so the blood on their hands would the multitudinous seas incarnadine. To strengthen ourselves against the power and reach that they have purely because of dodgy money from dodgy elites, let's remind ourselves that they are on the wrong side of the history. They are on the wrong side of the history that will be written if the history of our time gets to be written at all. They are a desperate rearguard action against the tide of truth.

One of the proudest and most consequential moments of my life was leading the charge, two years ago, right as we were forming XR, against the absurd continued presence of the Nigel Lawsons of this world[28] as 'balance' against climate truth; we won, the BBC ended its stupid policy of 'balance' between facts and alt-facts.

Progress is possible, my friends.

And so, the task is to end the rearguard action of the deniers as swiftly as possible; because the longer they are allowed to continue it, the more death there is in Pakistan, and in the Brazilian rainforests, and much, much more. Because they are helpful instruments to the elite in delaying life-saving action.

So then, friends and fellow rebels, let's take a moment, this moment, to commit to shining the light for as long and as unerringly as necessary, to reveal the blood on the hands of the Tufton tribe, and to uphold the truth itself as a gift as precious as the people and places whom these privileged liars are deeply complicit in the killing of.

The system, the death machine, is our enemy. Not human beings. Tufton Street plays a key role in that system. After today, many more people will know about that role, after today. Because we are the power. The power of truth.

So I want to end by saying thank you for playing your part in exposing the truth about the heart of darkness that exists here at Tufton Street.

Thank you.

Chapter 3
'What else would you have me do?'

My closing statement to the Magistrates' Court, London, in the trial of the 'Tufton Street Three'

A few hours after giving the speech 'We are power' (see Chapter 2) from the steps of 55 Tufton Street, under the very noses of the constables there to police the event, I engaged in non-violent direct action alongside Jessica Townsend (co-founder of Writers Rebel) and Clare Farrell (co-founder of XR), against the Global Warming Policy Foundation (GWPF). We daubed the front of their building with fake blood and with the slogan 'Lies, lies, economics, lies'. What follows is my impassioned and yet I hope also very reasoned closing statement to the magistrates a year later, at our trial on 28 October 2021. Having had our defence conducted by the brilliant lawyers of Hodge Jones & Allen, we dismissed them at the final stage of the trial so as to be able make our closing statements ourselves.

Our cases and our statements appeared to have worked. We were found guilty, but we were given the very lightest sentences possible: conditional discharges for six months for Criminal Damage (now expired; I am no longer a criminal). More tellingly still, the Court divided the costs of the damage such that the GWPF had to pay more towards clearing up the damage than we three did. The Court could scarcely have sent a subtler yet clearer signal of where their sympathies lay.

The case and the verdict attracted wide interest and fed into further scrutiny of the GWPF (now Net Zero Watch) and action against this so-called 'leading' remnant of climate denial.

First published by Writers Rebel[29]

Your Honour, may I start with one point of law. I wish to dispute the claim by the Prosecution that our action did not meet the criterion of addressing an 'imminent' threat to life. It is well-established in English law that 'imminence' does not only mean 'that very night' or the like. The classic example is its being accepted in law that if Anne Frank had stolen a car to escape from Amsterdam under Nazi occupation, the law of this country would not have held her guilty of a crime, and in particular that if a prosecutor argued that she should have waited until the Gestapo came knocking at her door before resorting to crime, that would have been a dangerous and excessively narrow interpretation of 'imminence', allegedly entitling her only then to the defence of necessity.

Our defence of necessity is that the Global Warming Policy Foundation represents an ongoing and ongoingly imminent threat to life in the same way Anne Frank faced. Every day, each and every single day that climate action is delayed by climate denialism and climate delayism[30] multiplies the threat that climate breakdown hangs over us all, over our very lives, over the future itself.

But in the rest of my remarks, I don't want to rehearse the legal arguments you have already heard from me and my lawyers. I want to do something different.

I want us to set aside our official roles, as much as we can.

I'm a philosopher by trade. My business is critical thinking and logic; in this way, my day-job is very like the law that you on the magistrates' bench are embodying here today.

I want to set all the rational arguments and the legalese aside, in these final five minutes, and address you directly, person to person, human to human. Because, sure, I'm here today because of my philosophy and because of the ethical demand upon me, and I'm here today because of the years I've spent working alongside the world's leading climate scientists. But most of all I'm here today because of my nephew and nieces. One of my nieces wanted to come and see the proceedings here today; she wasn't allowed into the courtroom, because she is too young. I did what I did that night in Tufton Street because I'm deeply scared and wounded whenever I contemplate what the world may well be like by the time she's all grown up.

The world into which my nephew and nieces are growing up may become nothing like this one; because of our chronic and criminal inaction on climate, there's a real and growing risk that all this [gesturing at the room] will be swept away. All the institutions we rely on, including yours, are now at risk. Law and order will likely break down, if climate breakdown causes civilisational breakdown, as is now on the cards.

You are intelligent, professional people; even before the evidence that we presented here earlier, I'm sure you've read about the IPCC reports. You probably know what I've been saying already. You know, deep down, that everything now hangs in the balance.

So my question for you is this:

Here I stand, I can do no other. I've tried everything else; you've heard in court today the record of the years I've spent tackling this intensifying emergency through my academic writing, through my political activism, through influencing central government, through being an elected representative myself and participating in local government. I had some small successes through some of this; and was part of a larger success when Extinction Rebellion moved the dial of opinion decisively in 2019. And you've heard how I've taken on the GWPF directly in debate, and how I led the successful campaign in 2018 to stop their 'top man' Nigel Lawson from being used as 'balance' to climate truth, on the BBC. And yet still these people at Tufton St, with influence even today at the very highest level,[31] …even now they try tirelessly to stop the alarm being raised adequately. What am I to do? What ought I to have done, if not what I did, knowing what I do, knowing what we know?

We've known from the start that the very strong likelihood is that you'll find us guilty. But I'm asking you now: what else would you have me do? Where else should I make my stand, if not as I did? And if not now, then when? Would you have us wait until the Thames barrier is overtopped? 'Til the Palace of Westminster is flooded out? Can you honestly tell me I should have waited even longer than I did, before finally undertaking non-violent direct action myself?

So…

Before making your final decision on our guilt or innocence, I want you to look into these eyes and ask yourselves honestly: what else would you have me do? I had to do something more to expose the deniers to the light; to stop them from any longer being able to stop the alarm from being adequately raised. If not this, then what? If not now, then when?

See this fellow human being standing, open, before you. Tell me truly that I acted too soon, if you can. What my heart and my conscience tell me is that, if anything, I left it too late.

Tell me, please: what would you have me do, if not what I did?

Chapter 4
'Act now *because* it's too late'

Speech to the August 2021 Extinction Rebellion

This is the full text of a speech I gave to a rally of thousands outside the Department for Business, Energy and Industrial Strategy (BEIS), Westminster, during the August 2021 Extinction Rebellion. The speech charts inter alia a potential path for XR beyond making demands of others and deeper into the territory of taking preparedness and resilience, aka 'adaptation', seriously, ourselves, as a consequence and a totem of cli-mate-truthfulness. (That path has not been taken by XR, and is now being taken by others, including the Climate Emergency Centres network and the Transformative Adaptation collective.)

The slogan of this rebellion is: 'Act now *because* it's too late.' You might reasonably ask: What on earth does that mean? Of course, it doesn't mean it's too late to do anything. It's never too late to do the right thing. It's never too late to reduce the harm. No matter how bad things get there will never be a point where it's possible for us to give up. So that's not what it means. So, what *does* it mean?

Well, what I think it means, first and foremost, is that the best time to have acted on this emergency was…well, about 50 years ago. The next best time was several years ago, and the next best time is right now.

But what that also implies is that it's too late to hold onto the hopes we could have had. I mean hopes for what the transition that we're going to go through will look like. It's too late to have the same hopes that we could have had for that if the transition had started 50 years ago or 10 years or even three years ago. It's too late to prevent appalling harm. It's too late to prevent the ongoing and worsening disasters, the weather driven berserk. It's too late, obviously, to prevent the loss of all the people who've died since we were last here outside this ministry because of this appalling long emergency, this endless new condition that we've been brought to, a condition that was preventable, but isn't any longer. It's too late to prevent those deaths. Climate chaos is here. This is not something for 2100 or 2050 or 2035 or even 2025; it is here. It is wreaking unprecedented death and devastation already, at just 1.2 degrees of global overheat. It's too late for that not to be the truth; that's the truth that we have to tell and that we have to face every day, and what that means is that it's now too late to *prevent* this 'emergency', this slow, endless, disastrous state of affairs that we've been shoved into. It's too late, too, to focus only on what's called 'mitigation': on reducing the greenhouse gases which are at the root of the trouble our atmosphere is in.

So XR now has this excellent, incredibly modest, immediate demand: stop all *new* fossil fuel exploration and production now. It really is such a moderate demand: who could possibly object to it? Not: stop *using* fossil fuels overnight. Just stop unearthing more of the stuff. We already have enough of it to fry ourselves twice over: how could we possibly need more? And you know, we might even be getting somewhere with that demand. It's becoming increasingly difficult for the government to retain any credibility while they plan to go ahead with their new coal mine in Cumbria. Now that the Greens are junior partners in the government in Scotland maybe there's a chance of stopping new oil exploration off Scotland. Maybe we'll get somewhere with this immediate demand.

But when I say that we have to acknowledge the ways in which it's already too late I mean that there needs to be another immediate demand as well; in addition to stopping new fossil fuel exploration, we need to have a crash emergency programme to cope with the damage that it's too late to prevent. From now on it's too late to have a focus only on prevention and precaution and what is called in the climate lingo 'mitigation', vital though those things are. We need to get serious about 'adaptation'.

This means getting serious about recognising that it is no longer credible to talk about *ending* or *solving* or *reversing* the climate crisis. What we need to do now and henceforth is realistically to focus on our vulnerability, on the need to adapt and, crucially, on the need to adapt in the right way. If we try to cope with heat-domes and unprecedented storms and rings of fire by building higher walls to keep these rising tides from coming and hitting us, it's not going to work. It's really not going to work. We've got to adapt to the damage that is already here and the worse damage that is already coming and we've got to adapt in a manner that is transformative.[32] We've got to roll with the punches *in a way that involves system change*. Yes, we've got to make ourselves resilient, we've got to make ourselves more food-secure and (where possible) food-sovereign, we've got to relocalise society, we've got to create flood defences which work with nature not against nature, we've got to restore wetlands, we've got to restore biodiverse habitats that can help us to absorb the water that is going to pour upon us with more and more frequency. We've got to adapt, but we've got to adapt transformatively. We've got to adapt in a way which mitigates and prevents at the same time; it's too late to do anything less.

So, we need to be demanding of this lot [gestures behind at BEIS], our so-called leaders, some of whom work in the building behind me. We need to be demanding of them not just 'no new fossil fuel' but a whole raft of new transformative adaptation measures to cope with our vulnerability. We need to be demanding of them that they put in place, now, ways of growing food that will be able to cope with the horrendous floods and fires and heat waves that are coming – it's too late for anything else but such demandingness. We need to relocalise, in the end, because we cannot depend any longer on the indefinite continuance of international flows of food and everything else continuing, in the uncertain, vulnerable future we are moving into.

And one more thing.

Can we really expect that our so-called leaders are going to deliver all of that?

[Crowd murmurs: 'No']

It's just not quite credible somehow, is it? You know, it's not telling the truth to say, 'Well it could happen, they could turn around overnight and do all of these things that I've just been enumerating.' So *it's too late for us to leave it all up to them.* We need to start doing this stuff for ourselves as well. What transformative adaptation, what really coping with our vulnerability is going to have to mean is, we need to take this power into our own hands, as citizens in places like Nepal and Rojava have already been doing, showing us the way. As well as demanding these changes from them we have to say, 'It's too late for us to trust that you're going to deliver them all, so we're going to start putting them in place ourselves.' Now that's truly demanding! But it clearly is too late for anything less. We need to start turning the agenda of the Transition Towns movement and the permaculture movement and so forth into a reality on the ground. *We* need to lead. To ourselves initiate serious action starting literally at the grassroots level. And if the powers that be try to stop that then we need to use non-violent direct action to make it happen, to support each other to make the kind of changes that we need to survive what's coming, what's already here and the escalating worse that's coming.

So, as we go forward through this rebellion and beyond it, I ask of you to demand not only that they leave the rest of the fossil fuels in the ground but to demand also that they start to make the kind of changes to cope with the disasters that are already here and that are coming; and if they don't respond to those demands, and *they will not* respond to them fully, then start to do it yourselves. Let's start to do it ourselves. To show that we mean business. That we are real power.

Perhaps you still want to know more about what exactly I mean when I say, 'Let's start to do it *ourselves*'. Let me say a little more about that, before I move to a close. I'm talking about moving beyond just making demands of others; I'm talking about manifestation, pre-figuration, being the change we want to see in the world. I'm talking about ac-tually creating readiness, on the ground. For our government is not only failing utterly on reducing greenhouse gas emissions; it is failing even worse[33] – and that's saying something! – on creating resilience to, *preparedness* for, the coming climate disasters: the off-the-scale heatwaves, the wildfires, the 'biblical' epochal floods and storms, and more. They are not keeping us safe; they cannot be trusted to do so; so we the people must step forward and start to lead, hard though it is, on co-creating such safety. Such safety as we can. They are making us vulnerable; it is not enough to fulminate against this, we need to actually address our own vulnerability, reduce it. How can we do this? You already *know* how. We can do it by building community, so that we are ready to help each other and especially the most vulnerable, when the times come. This effort can build on the fantastic mutual-aid endeavours that sprang up during COVID-19. We can do it by growing food together in ways that are at least partly insured against extreme weather; by stockpiling water; by growing under cover as well as in the open air; by diversifying crops and varieties to include more drought-resistant, heat-resistant, *and* flood-resistant varieties. And we can do it by spreading awareness and skills – for example, through the embryonic but spreading network of Climate Emergency Centres.

We can do it.

We must. Because it's past time to take such resilience-building, such transformative adaptation to the coming climate hell-times, into our own hands.

I'll draw to a close by saying this: this rebellion is an important moment; what we're doing here today, right here right now, this is important. The eyes of this country are upon us. But in November of this year the eyes of the world are going to be upon us. There is a moment in history that is coming, an event taking place in Glasgow that is more significant than any event that has taken place in this country for a long, long time, probably for generations. COP26.

Why is it important? It's important because the governments of the world have the chance to stop this decline from going any further – and it's important *because they are not going to take that chance.* 'Led' by the UK Government, who have the COP Presidency, they are going to fail us. I'm sorry to have to say this bitter truth very bluntly but there's no time left to spare for anything but the truth. The Glasgow COP is going to fail us. It might fail us a bit more or less badly, but it is going to fail us. The moment in history that we have in store, what today is, above all, the preparation for, is when this coming COP *ends.* Then, there is an opportunity for a huge wake-up call, for a far greater number of people than are assembled here today to wake up and to be mobilised and to demand those mitigation and prevention measures that we so badly need, and to demand real, strategic adaptation, to demand that we deal with our growing vulnerability… and if – *when* – those demands are not heeded, to start to do it themselves, to start to do it ourselves.

History is going to be made this November not by the governments who are going to fail us; it's going to be made by us. Let us go forward from today with the solemn intention that whatever we achieve or do not achieve today and the rest of this week and next week, we will use as the basis for something of much greater significance still. I want to urge you to come to Glasgow in November. Be there for the middle if you can, be there for the start if you can, but whatever you do, be there at the end. Be there at the end to mark the moment in history of their failing us, the moment when we get to say to the world, 'Rise up and join us and transform the future because they have failed us and now it's up to us.' That is what it's going to be about this November; that is the moment in history that is waiting to happen this November.

So please, friends and comrades, whatever we achieve or do not achieve here today, plan on being there in Glasgow, Friday November the 12th, and if you can't be there in Glasgow be here in London, or in any and every capital city in the world. We need people to rise up on that day and say, 'They have failed us; *we* are taking charge of history now; we are going to make the transformation start to happen – because it's too late for anything less.'

Thank you![34]

Chapter 5
The power of confessing *our* historic failure: Introducing GreensCAN, the Greens' Climate Activists Network

The Greens should be undertaking electoral politics and carefully executed, mass, targeted non-violent direct action. We are well placed to do this. That is a key practical take-away from this piece. But the piece has a wider aim too: to explore the game-changing power of the truth-telling undermining such a course of action.

This piece was aimed primarily at Green Party voters/supporters/members, especially in the UK. It predicts the failure to salve our predicament of COP26, and calls for a new politics of paradox[35] where our greatest power is the power of the powerless:[36] the power to name our own failure, achieve resonance with one's audience, and thus, from a new authentic beginning thoroughly grounded in this truth-telling, embrace radical hope – the hope that begins when old hopes are admitted to be dead. It calls for Greens to return to their radical roots. The beauty of the new situation, with XR and Greta Thunberg having moved the Overton window, is that this would still be Greens(CAN) being a moderate flank relative to Extinction Rebellion.

This is a lightly edited version of the article first published in Green World, *on 16 December 2020.*

In 2019, Antonio Guterres, UN Secretary General, said that we had until the end of 2020 to get a plan underway to deal with the climate crisis or there was no way we would hit the necessary targets for this coming decade.

2020 is at its end [at the time of writing]. It's time for some straight talking. Guterres has begun that straight talking by stating last week that we humans have broken our planet by way of unleashing a 'suicidal war' on nature.

The least Greens can now do is be as serious in our truth-telling and act accordingly. For the situation is indeed truly grisly.

We are not going to hit the necessary targets. We are on track to miss[37] the already grossly inadequate Paris climate targets[38] by a country mile. The world is heading for 3 to 4 degrees of global overheat, perhaps within the lifetimes of some of us, and probably within the lifetimes of some of our children. Therefore, *this* civilisation is coming to an end, one way or another. This does not mean it is game over for civilisation, as such. It means it is game over for this civilisation: *this* way of organising things is coming to an end. We transform, fast, or we go down. (Or, possibly, both.)

The COVID-19 pandemic, which is itself a product of the eco-emergency[39] and of the out-of-control neoliberal globalisation driving it, has, with all its lockdowns, put only a very small dent into this dire prognosis. The reset from COVID-19 will determine humanity's path for this decade and therefore for this century. The signs are very poor that this reset will be anything like what we need. And much of that reset is already set.

The Glasgow climate COP, which was unfortunately delayed for a year (due, of course, to COVID-19), is going to fail. If it delivers an agreement at all, it will be an inadequate one. It will contain lots of dire stuff, including recommendations for large-scale ecosystem-destructive biofuels, and IOUs written on the bodies of future generations, 'promising' to – or promising that *they* will have to – remove lots of carbon from the atmosphere using unproven and frankly reckless technologies.

Deep breath. The dream that motivated the Green Party, the dream of achieving power by the electoral route in time to prevent eco-disasters... is dying. We now have only five to 10 years left in which to transform our entire system, or face nemesis. Is there anyone who seriously believes that the Green Party can take power in that time period and make the necessary changes? Essentially, that would mean winning the 2024 general election. That is pure fantasy.

The Green Party needs a new dose of realism about the state of play in the 2020s and needs to go back to its roots. We need to double-down on the real issues, the issues that our children will ask us about and judge us on: the ecological emergency in general, and the climate crisis in particular.

If we back up such new realism with a deepened willingness to engage in carefully targeted non-violent direct action, as leading Greens have on occasion already done, then the message will have extra credibility. We will be showing by our deeds that we mean what we say. We should be proud of the fact that we are the one Party to have such civil disobedience in our Philosophical Basis.[40] The systems crisis we are living through needs combating by passionate commitment to life on Earth. That is shown by deeds meeting words.

The word 'carefully' in the above paragraph is key. XR was a brilliant pathfinder. But in actions at Canning Town and at Trinity College Lawn, it fatefully undermined its 'brand', and guaranteed a ceiling to its own appeal. By contrast, if we look back over the much more sporadic but much longer history of Greens undertaking NVDA, there are in my view no comparable own-goals. Whereas there are striking cases where the public has been won over, such as Caroline Lucas being found not guilty of a criminal offence in relation to her civil disobedience against fracking, and Green Councillor Alison Teal winning big through standing up directly for Sheffield's trees. This is what I have in mind as the GreensCAN strategy: rigorous truth-telling, larded with carefully targeted NVDA which demonstrates congruence, and with less risk of self-sabotage than has occurred in XR. This is how the Green Party could find a way forward that fits our time.

The Green Party is not going to attain power through a conventional electoral route. This is the painful reality that life is calling upon us to acknowledge.

Now, for the good news: there is one very real power that the Green Party has. *Within the field of electoral politics*, we are the trusted messengers when it comes to climate. We 'own' the green area of the political agenda. The real power we have therefore is *to call it*. To name the truth that the dream of arresting dangerous human-caused climate change is dead. That conventional politics has failed. That we have to turn to people-power, and to aim for adaptation and not just mitigation.

Our doing this will be all the more powerful and deeply authentic if it is accompanied by us being courageous enough to admit that there is not a Green Government-in-waiting for Number 10 Downing Street. People will really listen to us if they hear us breaking the 'rules' of politics by not just saying something that talks up our own electoral prospects. And citizens are hungrier than ever for that kind of honesty in politics.

So, here's the beauty of this bold proposal. We could carry on doing what we are doing, attempting a long march through the electoral institutions, but we know in our hearts that it won't be enough. But the proposal made *here* is the one that just might conceivably be enough!

For the one way we could conceivably set up the mother of all Green surges, the one way we could utterly transform politics, is if we break through into people's consciousnesses with an unexpected, true, authentic message backed by action. Unexpected and stark because no one expects a politician to say, 'We are not about to win at the ballot box.' Paradoxically, the one way we might unleash the Green Party with a new power at the ballot box is by saying plainly to voters that the ballot box alone is no longer enough!

We are the electoral wing of the broad green movement and should remain so. What my colleague Councillor Alison Teal has modelled in Sheffield – by her willingness to be arrested defending the trees there, which led to her massive re-election – is that, contrary to some lazy thinking, non-violent direct action that is intelligent, targeted, and makes sense to local people can be enormously popular. If we come clean about our future electoral prospects and the impending failure of the UK-led COP, and start being leaders – in our own name – of the coming mobilisation to save our common future, then, ironically, that is the one way we might transform our electoral prospects.

What Alison and others have done in Sheffield is in effect to prove in advance that the GreensCAN model can work.

So, Greens should be undertaking electoral politics *and* carefully executed, mass-targeted non-violent direct action. We are surely the people best placed to do this. We are the only force in politics set up to tell the truth and be heard, on this one seminal issue. If we do, it will be game-changing. If we don't, then we will be at best a minor footnote to, and more likely in the dustbin of, history.

The matter is in your hands, Greens. If you agree with the diagnosis here, then join us: me, Alison Teal, Shahrar Ali, Laura Baldwin, Tina Rothery, and others. We have high-profile sympathetic voices on record too, including Jonathan Porritt, Peter Tatchell, Sarah Lunnon, and (wait for it) Caroline Lucas. We have set up a new network: the Green Party Climate Activists Network. Because we believe – even yet, even now – that the Green Party *CAN*.

Chapter 6
GreensCAN, but it ain't easy...

This piece, published in Green World on 23 December 2021, a year on from the piece reproduced in Chapter 5, assesses the limited impact of GreensCAN on the political/Green landscape. This is a case study in how the politics of truth is slow, and hard. Do we want to hear the whole truth? Unsurprisingly, it turns out that a big part of us often doesn't.

The message of this book is a message that people are only just becoming able to hear. This is very frustrating in a time when urgency is paramount. But that, too, has to be accepted. It is yet another datum for why we are not going to get the transformation we need on schedule; for why a serious emphasis on bottom-up, transformative, deep adaptation (and indeed on loss and damage) is unavoidable. For why we have to go yet further into the pain, and into the truth: including the truth that even the call to face the truth is as yet not being adequately heard.

It's exactly a year since GreensCAN, the Greens' Climate Activist Network, publicly launched.

It's been a fascinating year for us. A lot of significant names have come on board and we had an impact on the debate around COP26, in part by demonstrating clearly how COP was failing us.[41]

I think it is safe to say that, in the wake of COPs having failed humanity and failed the future, my colleagues and I are more convinced than ever that the GreensCAN strategy is basically right. That is to say: The Green Party and the broader green movement can and must learn from the towering success of XR and Greta: that authentic truth-telling about the ecological and climate emergency is the key to making headway at this vital, pivotal, and terrible moment in history. The Green Party should join in – crucially, by coming clean that the parliamentary road to ecologism is no longer viable on its own. We have to face our own failure, along with the failure of the entire system with which we are entangled. Such an admission of failure is potentially game-changing; it is the power of the powerless; it is immense.

The politics of our time is a politics of paradox – if we admit openly that we are in grief and reassessment due to our deepest hopes of a smooth transition having come to nought, then we suddenly have an audience, an authenticity; a chance. In admitting that it's five *past* midnight, we can then pivot to a worthwhile form of adaptation, and finally face the difficult future coming down the track at us.

One mark of our seriousness in this switch will be a willingness, in alignment with the Philosophical Basis of the Green Party, to engage in non-violent direct action, congruently with the scale of the crisis, in order to exert greater pressure to prevent, mitigate, and adapt. Greens will no doubt only do this – as Caroline Lucas, Jonathan Bartley, and myself, among others, have sought to do – in a proportionate and wise way. We will thereby function as a moderate flank to the sometime-excesses of Extinction Rebellion (let alone of Insulate Britain).

We are more convinced than ever that roughly the path just outlined is the way to go. But what has become clear to us over the year since we launched is how difficult it is for people to accept this approach; because accepting it requires a shocking grieving and mourning process.

Such acceptance is extremely hard for Greens, many of whom, like myself, have spent big chunks of our life seeking to be elected, and, in the case of elected politicians, doing what one can within the system to make things better. It is really tough to face up emotionally and intellectually to the stark and bitter reality, the reality that it is too late for Greens to come to power through election and thereby save the world in the way we used to dream of and plan toward. Greens can hope to influence things through being elected, as we already do in this country and are doing somewhat more so right now in Germany;[42] but it is no longer credible to put all one's eggs in this aged basket.

49

It is also hard to ride more than one horse at once. Hard, that is, to say, as we do say and need to say, 'It's time to stand for election *and* engage in non-violent direct action *and* move bottom-up to undertake adaptation. As Greens.'

We are convinced the GreensCAN strategy is basically right… and we have come reluctantly to the view that it is going to take quite a long time for most Greens to admit that this is true. It is gutting to have to accept that the hope that motivated one's political life is not going to be realised sufficiently to avert horrors. And it is desperately difficult, downright painful, to face the fact that any hope of staying under 1.5 degrees is basically gone.

But the longer we leave it before admitting all this, the longer we keep citizens stuck in a dead game, a hall of mirrors. You only get to escape the hall of mirrors – into a land of greater truth, where there will be big new possibilities for action and movement-building – if you let go of the illusions that keep us stuck. *Illusions* such as this: that the Green Party will save the world through being elected soon. Or, that we are going to achieve staying within 1.5 degrees of over-heat, because we have to.

The 2020s will see swathes of new converts to the climate cause, and almost certainly swathes of new Green voters. Do we meet them with the old, fake story of 'Yes we can! It's all going to be fine; we'll 'fix' this!', and see them burn out after a year or two in bitter disappointment? Or do we dare to speak the truth to them: that we are in the age of consequences; that as a consequence transformative (and deep) adaptation is of equal importance to mitigation (i.e., to greenhouse gas emissions reduction); that everything is *not* going to be OK; that the eco-'emergency' is a permanent condition now; that damage-limitation is the order of the day; and that the only thing our kids will really care about when they speak to us in 20 years' time – the *only* thing – is whether we faced the crisis resolutely and with determination to do all we possibly could when there was still time. That resolution does not come from a desperate, fragile, 'Tell me how we fix this! Give me hope!' mentality. It comes from a clear-eyed appraisal of what we have to let go of, what we can still seek realistically and with determination to save, and how we are not just going to talk: we are going to *do* it.[43]

We now think, sadly, that it will be a couple more years before the Party, the movement, and the country are ready to really hear all this, take it in, and act accordingly.[44]

But mark my words: the sooner this is heard and felt, the better the future that remains to us all will be.

A final thought. Just as the GreensCAN message is hard to hear, and likely to be resisted, so is the 'meta-message' about it, contained in this very piece. If *you* find yourself resisting what I have been seeking to say here, then do please remember that. Reflect on it.

Only the truth can set you free, but it can only set you free if you decide to let it in. The only thing harder than waking someone up is awakening someone who is steadfastly *pretending* to stay asleep, someone *deliberately* endeavouring to remain prone in spite of everything.

Chapter 7
'COP26 has killed the goal of limiting global overheat to 1.5°C'

Speech given to delegates and press inside COP26

I gave this speech to delegates and the media at a UN Press Conference held inside the official 'blue' zone at COP26 in Glasgow, 12 November 2021. This was the moment when I 'called it' inside the belly of the machine: 1.5 is not alive.

I want to make a bold claim here today. Bold, but, I think, true.

This COP will go down in history as the COP that killed 1.5 degrees. It is not true that 1.5 degrees has been kept 'alive' by this COP, as COP President Alok Sharma has claimed; it's not even on 'life support' as far as I'm concerned. The analyses of the Climate Action Tracker and the UNEP Emissions Gap Report addendum are clearly showing that when you take into account what is realistically offered by this COP, then we are heading for closer to 3 degrees and it is no longer possible, credible, or even remotely sensible to let them get away with saying that that's a way of keeping 1.5 degrees alive.

When I read the draft agreement the other day I was actually shocked, I've got to admit it to you. I feel almost scandalised about myself to say that, because I've been warning for months about how ineffectual this COP is going to be, but even I wasn't expecting something as vapid as the actual document. There's basically nothing in it. Nothing by way of commitments. All it says is we want to try to do this, that, and the other *in the future*, and we promise to report yearly henceforth rather than five-yearly. It is simply an exercise in kicking the can down the road; that's it. We are supposed to be thrilled that the governments have promised now to report progress and goals annually. But what is the good of yearly reporting if what gets reported is mostly just 'promises' of *future* action?

The draft COP26 agreement is nothing but a can-kicking exercise. And given *that*, we must conclude that 1.5 degrees is no longer credible. This is a terrible thing to have to say, it sticks in my throat to say it, but I think it's nothing but the truth.

Because of the recalcitrance of a substantial number of countries, COP26 has failed us, and it has failed our children, who are left begging for their lives. And in the light of that I want to raise a couple of uncomfortable questions.

My first question is this: Sure, we can point our fingers at the fossil fuel industry and at the countries who are 'leading the way' in not showing any leadership, and there are other villains as well that we could point to, *but what about our own role in this?* Are those of us who have been strong critics of the COP process in some sense legitimating it by way of being here? I'm honestly not sure what the answer to this question is, but it seems to me that we have reached the point where we need at least to ask the question. We can no longer assume that taking part in this can-kicking exercise actually makes sense.

And my second uncomfortable question is this: if there's anything right about my first uncomfortable question, then *should there be more COPs?*[45]

It will be said in response, 'But look, the COP process may be dire but it's better than having no process at all and it does at least supply some kind of legitimacy and international law to give succour to claims from protesters in courts and so forth'. I get that, but what I'm asking is, *Do* the benefits at this point actually outweigh the costs? Would it be better to say, 'It's not one minute to midnight, it's not midnight, it's five past midnight'? At five past midnight, do we carry on these meetings that pretend that conventional hope is still alive?

Or do we start afresh? Perhaps with a breakaway strategy of countries that are actually serious about making progress on climate, and willing to be tough on countries that are not. The COP system has failed; arguably it was *designed* to fail[46] – it never had any sanctions built into it as, for example, the Montreal Protocol addressing the hole in the ozone *did*. There's never been any way of enforcing anything that's been happening in climate COPs these last 25 years…so should it actually carry on?

If you think that the thrust of what I've been saying is true, then we must take the first steps of fully claiming our agency and no longer outsourcing it to governments and the intergovernmental process. What's the implication of that? Well, right here in Glasgow we need to find some strong way of asserting that we recognise that it's five minutes past midnight, that we acknowledge the awful truth that our governments are not planning to save us, and that we intend to take back the power that they have abdicated using. What *that* means in very micro terms, it seems to me, is that not just outside the official COP blue zone but here *inside* the blue zone we should consider protesting. We should consider walking out.[47] We should consider joining those who are protesting outside the exits. We must mark and narrate this infamous moment in human history; the moment when 1.5 degrees became consigned to history and where it became clear that no one's coming to save us. It's up to *us* now.

Chapter 8
The can stops here:
On the Glasgow COPout

Towards the end of COP26, I reported for the Eastern Daily Press *and* Brave New Europe *on the COPout in Glasgow – and on the wonderful walkout that responded to it. This is an updated, enriched, and expanded version of that reportage.*

There's a phrase used in politics, 'to kick the can down the road'. It means to put off confronting a difficult issue or making an important decision until a later date – and it perfectly sums up what's happened at COP26.

It had been described as 'our best last chance' but instead of taking it, the gutless message governments have given each other is, 'Go away, have a think, and come back next year to let us know.' The bitter truth is that virtually everything in the agreement hatched at Glasgow consists of empty promises or exhortations to do better next time.

Can you hear the noise of the can tumbling away down the street?

Well, guess what? This time someone has stuck their foot out and stopped it rolling. In fact, lots of someones, gathered in Glasgow and across the world said, 'Nope, not today.' I'm talking about the inspiring walkout from COP26 that thousands in the official 'blue zone' staged on the final day of the COP, Friday November 12. Dignifiedly exiting a process that has categorically failed. Failed all of us.

How did it come to this? For months I had been warning that COP26 was not going to be the great planet-saving game-changer I know so many were hoping for. 'A bad deal is better than an awful deal or no deal at all,' I said,[48] trying to manage expectations; but even I was shocked at what actually happened.

When I read the early drafts of agreement proposals published on Wednesday, they took my breath away with their inadequacy. The contents of these pitiful documents were to be our approach to turning back the fast-ticking clock?

At the start of COP26, Boris Johnson talked about it being 'a minute to midnight'. Very well. By that reckoning, it must now be *past* midnight. For the clock can't always be poised at just before midnight. Sometimes one has to admit that time has passed and opportunities have gone forever.

This COP, at Glasgow, was the one. The COP that was supposed to fulfill the mandate of Paris. And the COP that happened to be timed to co-enact the post-COVID-19 resetting.

It won't do, to seek to divert the can straight onto COP27. No, this time a reckoning must be reached. For COP26 is another nail that this civilisation drove into its own coffin. Another piece of *permanent* self-inflicted damage. Every one of these fails – such as the failure by Government to take full positive advantage of the Extinction Rebellion, the fail to utilise the COVID-19 crisis as a moment to truly transition our economy and values to green [the same fail in the case of the invasion of Ukraine] is in certain key respects an irreversible fail. These moments never come again. Time has an arrow and the CO_2 clock too keeps ticking onwards as its graph rises.[49]

Let's be concretely clear about what the gross failure at Glasgow means: You can forget limiting global temperature rises to 1.5°C above pre-industrial levels. Climate Action Tracker reckons Glasgow as putting us on track for 2.7 degrees of global over-heat![50] That is potentially terminative of our civilisation. The new UNEP 'emissions gap' report has it at 2.8.[51] These figures are almost double 1.5°C. They are utterly unsafe.

Glasgow is where 1.5 was taken off life-support. This means that a lot more people are going to be killed.

Even the weak Glasgow draft text itself expressed 'alarm' that emissions were far higher than the levels needed to stay within any remotely safe threshold. The terrible truth is that those charged with keeping us safe are making us vulnerable. They have betrayed our trust.

The British Government tried to achieve a 'Yes we can!' vibe at Glasgow. Much of the world's media, including, strikingly, the BBC, went along with this. But the truth is that this is just another forlorn version of '1 minute to midnight'. Any even-remotely-honest analysis of the situation makes plain that this COP has failed us, and that kicking the can down the road a year, as they are doing on emissions-reduction pledges and much more, is merely a ploy to distract our attention.

So: we must refuse to be distracted. Their 'Yes we can' is a lie. 'No we can't' is more like it. They are subtly admitting that they can't or won't do it. That they can't bring themselves to act responsibly.

The can stops here…

Just when I thought all hope was lost, people came through. The mass walkout from COP26 was heartening; but even that is not enough.

Now we need to build on it; we need to be willing to demand our governments pick up that can and never let it roll away again. And if, as is likely, they mostly won't, then we'll get on, bottom-up, and do it ourselves…

The world will never be the same. Not because of what our 'leaders' didn't or couldn't or wouldn't, but because of what *we* do…

For now, that means we need to recognise that it's five past midnight, there's clearly no more time to waste pretending, outsourcing, or waiting.

After COP, it will mean co-creating the much larger mobilisation that is now needed. To pressure governments much more. And to start to *make*, ourselves, the changes they apparently can't.

Chapter 9
An open letter to Michael Mann: Let the new climate war not be … between us

Michael Mann is one of the world's best-known climate scientists. Perhaps as a result of having been subject to an awful long campaign of target-ing from climate denialists, he has something of a habit of being on a hair-trigger when it comes to criticism or even just debate. At the end of COP26, BBC Radio 5 Live set up a debate between him and me on whether the summit had been successful: him arguing it had been, me arguing it hadn't. Unfortunately, he refused to debate me. Instead, they interviewed him, and then me, sequentially. You can hear my side of the 'exchange' in the recording of the event.[52] I argue in it that Mann is not telling the truth when he looks wildly on the bright side of recent developments such as COP26. He is not accepting the invitation implicit in the entire book you are reading.

I wrote the piece that follows in response to Mann's unprovoked attack on me in his book The New Climate War. *That attack was the kind of thing I had long expected; thankfully, it has been relatively rare from 'allies', much more common from the usual suspects – deniers, delayers, and the like. I include this piece because the affair nicely exemplifies the resistance to and the risks of a resolutely truth-centric approach – and because I hope to show in this response how one can remain in a spirit of inclusivity and sol-idarity, even when faced with attempts to fragment, intimidate, or negate.*

Dear Michael,

In your book *The New Climate War* you call for an overcoming of the 'tribalism' that has come to shadow the debates around climate. In that spirit, I'm writing to you today in a vein of open and civil discussion. I hope earnestly for your response in the same way.

In your book, while praising Extinction Rebellion [XR] in some important respects, you also criticise them for allegedly adopting a 'soft doomest' frame at times. Here is what you say, citing a quotation from XR as alleged evidence to back up that criticism:

> 'Soft doomism has become increasingly widespread. Its basic tenets have been adopted by groups like Extinction Rebellion, which takes the position that 'we are facing an unprecedented global emergency. Life on earth is in crisis … [W]e have entered a period of abrupt climate breakdown, and we are in the midst of a mass extinction of our own making.'
>
> Excerpt from *The New Climate War*

I really want to understand why you think this constitutes a kind of '[soft] doomism', Michael. It seems to me, by contrast, simply a plain telling of the terrible truth, virtually indistinguishable from, say, David Attenborough's remark: 'If we continue on our current path, we will face the collapse of everything that gives us our security: food production, access to fresh water, habitable ambient temperature, and ocean food chains…and if the natural world can no longer support the most basic of our needs, then much of the rest of civilisation will quickly break down.' You don't, presumably, take Sir David to be 'doomist' in his framing; so why use this epithet in relation to XR?

By 'soft doomism' you mean distortion of the climate science that makes it sound as if we are doomed. The only bit in the statement from XR that you call 'doomist' that could conceivably match that description is 'abrupt climate breakdown'. You leap to the conclusion that this must mean something like the 'Methane dragon', which you take to be a non-existent threat. I don't take it to be a non-existent threat. We are starting to see alarming signs of the vicious feedback emerging of methane release from polar regions, etc.

But leave that point on one side, for the sake of argument; the methane dragon may or may not appear. In terms of interpreting the remark from XR, why not assume what I take the phrase 'abrupt climate breakdown' to mean, namely: simply *a ramping up* of what we have already been *experiencing* in the past few years. Dramatic actual/potential shifts in weather and climate, such as a worsened form of the scary disruption in Arctic weather systems that we have been seeing recently. The terrible, utterly unexpected, unprecedented heat-dome over North America in 2021, that resulted from that kind of jet stream meltdown, then looks like an instance, scarily, of abrupt climate breakdown. If the climate chaos we have been seeing in the last few years gets significantly worse over the coming decade, that may well, tragically, deserve the moniker 'abrupt climate breakdown'.

And after all, roughly this is just what the situation in the Arctic has indeed been called, in scientific papers in recent months and years, of which I am sure you are aware.[53]

The word 'abrupt' is hardly XR's invention. What XR are seeking to do, with science (and precaution) as the basis, is to *raise the alarm* about the direness of the more-than-emergency we are in, to help motivate action. I comprehend that, as a practising scientist, you might prefer to use a slightly different, 'calmer' rhetoric yourself, but it is unfortunate if you couch such a preference by way of using epithets such as 'doomist' to mis-characterise those who are actually engaged on the ground, at the grassroots, in the brave and vigorous effort to shake populations and governments out of their complacency.

Moreover, your preference for less mobilising rhetorics itself requires justification. You appear in your book to be concerned that by discussing very bad outcomes, and mobilising emotions on the back of those discussions, Extinction Rebellion and others could create a sense of hopelessness. But the question of whether you are correct in that assumption is of course a question of psychology (and of contemporary political history), not of climate science. The remarkable success of Extinction Rebellion, especially in the UK, suggests that forthright framings can succeed in galvanising. Consider as Exhibit 'A' here the very name 'Extinction Rebellion', which many initially assumed would doom the organisation to failure.

Add to this that the psychological evidence[54] itself does not appear on balance to support your assumption; rather, it suggests that frank truth-telling and the mobilisation of difficult emotions can be more effective at fostering real action than a calmer turn of phrase. This is perhaps why some in the scientific community take a very different view from you about the appropriateness of stark truth-telling about our predicament.

In sum: it seems divisive of you to assume that the XR statement above is 'doomist', rather than being a courageous and effective warning of the clear risk of the climate chaos we currently face becoming significantly worse. This is especially so given that XR *exists* in order to warn of and forestall the doom that, as Attenborough remarks, awaits us unless we change everything fast.

Your book contains not only the criticism of XR that I have sought to re-but above, but also a specific criticism of me. I have argued for some time that our society is fragile, vulnerable to shocks cascading from wholesale habitat destruction and from climate disasters, and that therefore we are at risk of worsening climate-/eco-disasters causing societal breakdown, perhaps within a generation or two. I think that such a warning is prudent as well as truthful. I don't think we are doing our kids any favours if we pretend that this kind of outcome is not even possible.

Because I do this (and because it appears that you assume, falsely, that I am *relying* on something like the 'methane dragon' hypothesis to back up my concern about the fragility of our food systems etc. in the face of a rising tide of climate chaos), in your book you call me out as a 'doomist'. I assert the painful truth that societal collapse as a cascading effect of climate chaos and ecosystems destruction, within a generation or so, can no longer be ruled out. Here is part of what you say about me:

> 'One of the more baleful aspects of doomism is the way it endorses intergenerational inequity – that is to say, its total dismissiveness when it comes to the interests of future generations. Rupert Read is an academic from the University of East Anglia in the United Kingdom and a self-avowed spokesperson for Extinction Rebellion. He's also a messenger of doom.'
>
> - Excerpt from *The New Climate War*

It is pretty astonishing to find myself accused of 'endorsing intergenerational inequity' when, for the last 20 years, central to my academic work has been a series of arguments both logical and passionate against the vicious generational inequity that we are all now complicit in.[55] It is even more astonishing, for the same reason, to be labelled as totally dismissive when it comes to the interests of future generations! This is the *polar opposite* of what my life's work has been about. Perhaps it is just possible that you didn't familiarise yourself with what I actually do and say before making the claim against me in your book, Michael.

I have spoken passionately, repeatedly, on national TV in favour of our taking the strongest possible action to safeguard future generations. I fight tooth and nail (non-violently) for my nephews and nieces and all the children of the world, and of the future. My personal philanthropy too has been almost wholly devoted to this cause. I was arrested for criminal damage for protesting against the lies and distortions of climate denialism, and prosecuted; I have only recently ceased to be regarded by the judicial system in the UK as a criminal. In short, I devote my life to trying to *arrest* our business-as-usual path towards calamity. If I am a 'doomer', I have a funny way of showing it!

Yet you call me 'a messenger of doom'. That is quite literally turning the truth on its head. Every single talk I give (including when I speak to kids) is a call to radical action: my prime endeavours are in favour of an 'emergency' programme of mitigation and to *transformative* adaptation to the impacts that are already here. You also describe my talks as 'fatalistic'. I am *never* 'fatalistic'; I am always completely the opposite. I can only assume that you have never actually heard me speak.

It is incredibly painful to feel obliged to say to children that they are not being kept safe, and that their future is no longer assured. That only if we rise up to protect them, to mitigate on an urgent basis *and* to adapt transformatively, will they have a modicum of security again. But I do it because it is true, and because I have been inspired by their uprising of the last few years. When I speak to youth climate strikers, they tell me to carry on telling the truth as I see it; because they are fed up with false reassurances from adults that everything is going to be fine. The concern that societal collapse within a generation or so can no longer be ruled out is hardly the marginal view of cranks or 'doom mongers' any longer. Consider the recent warnings from 500 scholars that it is time to contemplate the possibility of societal collapse, among other evidence.[56]

As I see it, my job – our job – is to seek to stop these possibilities from becoming actualities. But to refuse to even think about them or talk about them won't help us stop them.

As I see it, anyone who claims to know for a fact that our civilisation will collapse within a generation is over-stepping what we can deduce from what we know, and risks fatalistically undermining our sense of agency. But equally, anyone who claims to know for a fact that our civilisation will *not* collapse within a generation or so is over-stepping what we can deduce from what we know, and risks undermining our sense of urgency.

So I put it to you, Michael, that my position and my framing is the antithesis of 'doomism'.

But what I say does have the consequence that we can no longer blithely *assure* our children of a future, regardless. Instead, we have to fight like hell to make sure that they have a future.

Let's remember here that climate decline is already killing hundreds of thousands per year. Far more than that, if one includes the deaths from eco-driven and probably climate-driven pandemics such as COVID-19. This tide of deaths is certain to rise for some time to come. How do we somehow assume that our own children are immune to it?

'Front-line' states such as Bangladesh are clearly vulnerable to climate-overwhelm within a generation or so. But we tend to complacently assume that the USA and the UK are not. Why do we assume this, when the evidence from COVID-19 throws into stark relief the fragility of the systems in these 'advanced' (over-complex and politically-deeply-troubled) countries of ours?

Consider, as one of a myriad possible examples, the climate-chaos-caused freeze in Texas in early 2021. This killed children (as well as adults). In the heart of your country, the USA itself. Surely there shouldn't be any taboo on saying so any longer, and on warning starkly that unless we get the situation under control, such tragic deaths are liable to increase, exponentially. The graph of such deaths will end up looking like a hockey stick; unless we manage, even now, at the 12th hour, to turn the situation around, through radical truth-telling and radical (as well as 'moderate') action.

Michael, it goes without saying that you have the best of intentions. And I respect your concern about the possible harmful effects of doomist voices. I agree with you that counsels of pure despair are harmful. I just want to invite you to think again about whether there is really any counselling of despair in some of those whom you have labelled as engaging in 'doomist' framing.

What is perhaps my best-known book is entitled 'Parents for a Future: How loving our children can prevent climate collapse. Does that sound anything like the gospel of a doomer?

I'd love you to read the book, as I have been reading yours. I think if you did, you would find that, though we have important differences in rhetoric, and in our level of concern about the possible consequences of climate chaos/breakdown for our societies during the next generation, we are quite clearly on the same side, at the level of fundamentals. That is why I have sought here to write to you in a spirit of openness and civility. I don't think your claim about XR using 'doomist' framing can be sustained. I think if you knew my record and my work you wouldn't call me a 'doomist' or a 'fatalist' either. Those are truly the last things I am.

The situation our civilisation is in is a desperately painful one. It is so very sad that we need to have these kinds of discussions at all. For humans, it's the worst possible thing, not to be able to reassure our children that they definitely have a future. My book is called 'Parents for a Future' because it is centrally about adults stepping up to take responsibility now, to ensure that our children *do* have a future. I don't think it should be taboo any more to say these kinds of things, hard though they are to face.

My teacher, Joanna Macy, says that a key reason why she carries on now (she is 93) is that she wants to help us not turn on each other, in these hardening times. Michael, we in the climate movement need each other. I was sorry when you blocked me on Twitter for trying civilly to have this discussion with you. Such blocking doesn't seem very collegial.

I disagree with important aspects of your book, *The New Climate War*. I think you shy away from telling the full truth about our situation; including, I think you don't come entirely clean about how big the societal transformation will be if we are going to avoid collapse, and I don't think you face head-on the possibility of some such collapse occurring. We don't have to agree about those things! But we can surely find a way of agreeing not to disagree using language that is basically vicious and deeply misleading.

Michael, thank you for your tireless proactive work to address the existential crisis facing us all. Our disagreements notwithstanding, it is really good to see the way that you call steadfastly and powerfully for adequate action, now. I am with you completely in the effort at proactivity and at managing to find a way through this terrible situation that humanity has dragged itself into.

You have put up with completely wrong, deeply unseemly abuse for many years from the denialists. At the time of the hack into UEA climate science emails in 2009, which of course prominently included an attack on your vital 'hockey-stick' discovery and presentation, I stood alongside the UEA climate scientists and helped behind the scenes with doing PR against the criminal hackers and the liars and the denialists. This included seeking to defend you, your work, and your reputation.

Let's not help out hard denialists *or* soft denialists (those who are hoping for a reprieve from having to act at speed and radically), who want nothing more than for us to spat among ourselves. So let me ask: How shall we have a dialogue, so that we don't help them out? We don't have to be perfectly aligned, obviously! But it makes sense to foreground the vast amounts of common ground between us, rather than indulging in the narcissism of small differences, which is surely an unaffordable luxury at the time of urgency we are in.

I was interested to note, in an interview with *The Guardian*[57] on your book, your candid admission that fatalistic doomism is more like a mood that anyone can fall into at times – including you. Let's see if we can help each other not be dragged into that dark place. The situation is dark enough as it is.

So: Can we try again?

Yours faithfully,
Rupert

Chapter 10
What is the main obstacle to the truth about climate breakdown being fully told and fully heard?

This chapter draws on and updates my much shorter piece published in ABC Religion and Ethics under the title, 'The inconvenient truth about telling the truth about climate breakdown'.[58] It also incorporates parts of an article of mine on Vaclav Havel, in The Ecological Citizen. It is perhaps the closest thing there is to a 'foundational piece', in the present work; by which I mean that it enters as deeply as I've ever done into the need for and consequences of a fundamental, non-negotiable outlook of truth-telling.

In this chapter, I offer an explanation as to why it is so difficult for nearly all of us, nearly all the time, to engage in the truth-telling (and truth-hearing) that lies at the root of the successes achieved in recent years by Extinction Rebellion (XR) and Greta Thunberg: that *it requires dropping the rhetoric of 'hope' that our current system is going to be saved.* I outline the key failing of our current system, this very unwillingness to confront reality. In other words, I suggest that possibly the most dangerous feature of the system that keeps our civilisation going is precisely its systemically blocking citizens from seeing that the system itself cannot be sustained much longer.

This is so dangerous because the further we go into overshoot, the worse the likely crash. As has been documented in relation to historical cases,[59] the highly unequal nature of our societies makes this process more vicious and deadly because in such cases elites can fool themselves (and parts of their populations) for longer. They tend to remain mostly unaffected, until it is way too late.

I draw strength, in confronting our predicament of systemic truth-lessness, from the successful endeavour of Vaclav Havel and others, confronting a relevantly similar, seemingly hopeless situation, in using the power of truth to liberate.[60] I suggest that human beings are much more resilient than is often admitted. In particular, advocates of maintaining the pretence that the current system can be saved don't tend to notice or absorb this pretty widespread resiliency. I suggest that we who trust in that resilience are the ones offering true hope: hope that is manifested in sufficient action, hope that does not outsource, or wait around for others to take care of us, but directly seeks to enact what is needed, whether by undertaking civil disobedience, or radically changing business models, or adapting in our communities on the ground transformatively to the now-endemic threat of climate disasters.

I conclude that we who appreciate the kind of points being made herein are actually the ones with faith in humanity – faith not only that most of us can cope with the truth being told, but that if we are so told, we will start to respond appropriately – and that a lack of such faith is *itself* the main obstacle to the truth about climate breakdown being fully told.

An obstacle that comes from within us

Four years after the launch of Extinction Rebellion and of the Youth Strikes For Climate, enormous strides have been made toward living in truth with regard to the greatest crisis that has ever faced humanity: the ecological and climate 'emergency'. Compared to where we were in 2018, the situation is far better: the public has woken up to a considerable extent; hard denialism is in headlong retreat; the media gives the crisis much more attention.

And yet, if hard climate denial is much weaker than it was (though it still, tragically, exists, and even has some reins of power, especially in the USA), 'soft' climate denial has grown; most of the public and virtually all politicians continue to buy into fantasies of endless economic growth and are not, it would seem, willing to prioritise climate and ecology over more 'immediate' concerns. New ways of delaying action, such as focusing on the 'costs' of acting now, are sought and promulgated. And the media still fails to give the crisis anything like *sufficient* in-depth or sustained attention. (Many of us now, for instance, when talking to pollsters will say that the climate issue is the central one facing us.[61] But is this reflected in the way most of us absorb the daily news-cycle, or in what we regard as a satisfying version of that cycle? No.)

And the weather, meanwhile, keeps spinning further out of control. For one of many examples: as this book goes to press (late summer 2022), the UK and Europe have been experiencing not just record-breaking but record-smashing heat, and wildfires. I have written quite a lot of these words while sweltering.

The situation, in these respects, is worse, perhaps far worse, than it was four years ago. The truth about climate breakdown is not acknowledged enough, let alone acted on enough.

A 'meta-emergency'

This chapter aims squarely at why this is the case. Why is it, in particular, that even many of those who understand the gravity of the situation best tend to shy away, when the crunch comes, from stating and confronting it in its full starkness? Including owning up to how far off the pace virtually everyone, including, crucially, the media and governments, still are. For this fact of course multiples the emergency: part of the full nature of the 'emergency' we are in is precisely that, even now, hardly anyone is really treating it *as* an emergency. Call this 'the meta-emergency'.

It is vital to own up to just how stark our shared predicament is. For consider this obvious and consequential point: if the public cannot depend on scientists, academics, thought-leaders, and activists to be straight with them, who can they depend upon?

I take it as self-evident that the key reason for the extraordinary and unpredicted success of XR, of Greta, and of similar trends around the world (Sunrise, Ende Gelände, Ultima Generazione, etc.) in the last few years has been their authenticity, their willingness to state the uncomfortable truth and draw and act upon the requisite conclusions, congruently. Thus, it is imperative that any and all actions that fall away from this truthfulness and authenticity be gently but firmly named and changed. *Whoever* so fails, even if that is we ourselves.

Clearly there are a number of key, powerful obstacles to the truth about climate breakdown being fully, properly told and heard. They include the power of fossil money, depressingly undemocratic partly-corporate-captured political systems, sheer inertia in the overall system, the corporate and super-rich ownership of most of the media (including of social media), the monetisation of attention-deficit, fear of being socially unusual (fear, that is, of the consequences of calling out naked emperors), and the serious psychological challenge for humans of being properly long-sighted, long-termist.

My argument here, though, is that there is an obstacle that comes more strongly from within us, 'the good guys', too, and that it might just be the most important obstacle of all to the truth being fully told and heard. That obstacle is our own lack of adequate faith in humanity, and our own consequent temptation toward insufficient truthfulness. I think that this obstacle is in fact present virtually everywhere: among well-intentioned people in business, the academic world, religion, politics – and activism itself.

The 1.5 shibboleth

Let us consider a clear example: there is a huge push to try to keep global temperature increase to below 1.5°C, understandably and, in a certain sense, quite clearly *rightly* so. For 1.5 is the accepted proxy for a reasonable degree of safety; for averting catastrophic (as opposed to 'merely' disastrous) climate change.

The consequences of breaching 1.5°C are going to be horrendous, *more* than disastrous. But most people who are well-informed think that the chances of us actually – successfully – remaining within 1.5 are now negligible: just 4% of IPCC climate scientists, speaking freely, in a recent *anonymous* poll in *Nature*, saw the Earth staying below 1.5°.

I suspect – in fact, in some cases I *know* – that there are a good number of environmental leaders, politicians, activists, not to mention academics, who are well aware that staying below 1.5°C is completely implausible. These people are, or should be, aware moreover that there is a real risk that directing all our efforts at staying below 1.5 has a number of potential negative effects: it risks burnout when activists give up in disappointment as it becomes increasingly obvious (as it will, in the next few years) that 1.5 is going to be breached;[62] it risks distracting us from the need to adapt, and to adapt in the right way, now, to a changed world; *and* it risks some entering into full headless-chicken mode in a desperation to stay below 1.5°, and countenancing options (such as reckless geoengineering 'solutions') that could cost us the biosphere.

And yet, how many IPCC climate scientists are willing to *follow the science* by saying publicly that 1.5 is basically out of reach already? That there just is no plausible pathway to actually staying below 1.5°C, any longer? And how many 'environmental leaders' are willing to do so, while trying to gee up their activists or fundraise from their followers?

Now, just because something is utterly improbable does not mean that it should never be aimed at. Our movements arguably exist precisely because we seek to make the apparently 'politically impossible' possible. But when it comes to physics, and when it comes, more tellingly still, to the inertia and path-dependency that governs infrastructure and political and governance systems, then a cold dose of realism is much-needed too.

It is already impossible, in terms of the physics of climate-systems, to guarantee keeping global temperatures below 1.5°C. It will fairly soon be impossible full-stop to avoid 1.5° being breached. So the only way in which it is possible to have a good shot at doing so would be if the world were joining, already, right now, in a full-spectrum emergency-style mobilisation to do so. That mobilisation would have to have taken form around the emerging 'post-COVID-19' revision of our economies, and around COP26 in Glasgow. *But it simply, obviously hasn't.*

This has to be admitted.

The IPCC, a notoriously conservative institution, has now virtually admitted it.[63] Its most recent report said that without 'rapid, deep and immediate emissions reductions across all sectors', staying below the 1.5 upper limit for the 'safe' zone will be impossible.[64] Think about that. Contemplate what the chances are of immediate deep cuts in all sectors across all countries of the world. At a time when the UK (which still has the COP presidency as I write) is planning to open new coal mines and oil fields; when the USA under Biden is approving more new fossil fuel mining than Trump did; not to mention what is happening in Brazil, or China, or…

I could go on. There is no need to. Any thinking person can see that we are not, in 2022, collectively, worldwide going to embark on 'rapid, deep' emissions reductions, immediately.

We can't go on pretending that there are endless last-chance saloons. By the time global temperatures have reached 1.49°C above pre-industrial levels, everyone will agree that we have left it too late to stay below 1.5. But actually the cut-off point comes much, much sooner, because of how long it takes for a planetary supertanker to turn around.

We ought to have the honesty and the willingness to face horrific (or even heroic) failure; to be willing to face facts *now*. Only facing our failure will facilitate the learning and unleash a path that could make possible greater success in the hard times to come.

For the avoidance of doubt: it is entirely horrific that hitting 1.5 degrees is now as good as certain.[65] It is a death sentence for many, especially in the Global South. It will be the basis of charges of criminal negligence and more in future courts. It is heartbreaking. It is, as we might put it, unacceptable.

But nevertheless…there it is. When the unacceptable becomes un-avoidable then there is no choice but to accept it, and to draw the full range of consequences. And in fact, this makes my very point: in continuing to project a future in which we allegedly stay 'safely' below 1.5°C, we remain in complicity with the elites who have steered us into this disaster-zone; everyone keeps pretending together. In playing along with the narrative of, 'It's not too late to stay in the safe zone', we soft-pedal on the fury that we ought to be feeling right now.

Whereas, to relinquish 1.5 brings us in touch with a painful power: the power of that anger, that grief; unadulterated, raw. Right now.

The situation is beyond desperate. It is understandable that many of us have fragile morale, and we are all aware of this, and are trying not to de-molish each others' morale. But think more deeply about what is involved here, if one believes, as I have suggested one should, that 1.5 degrees is now a completely improbable target and yet one continues to spend much time breathlessly urging others to campaign to stay below 1.5.

Is that not a form of deception? A form, in fact, of manipulation of others, whom one basically hoodwinks in order to seek to string out maximum action and energy for as long as possible? And furthermore, can one really be comfortable with the risks of burnout, of sidelining adaptation (not to mention loss-and-damage), and of being useful idiots for reckless geoengineering 'solutions', that 1.5-ism brings in its train? For to 'keep 1.5 alive', there will be increasing talk of throwing mirrors into space, and the like.

I think that those who in practice are engaged in a kind of deception of the public or their followers in what has been a good cause – the cause of seeking to stay below 1.5°C – are missing the adventure. They are missing the awesome truth that XR and the school strikers have led the way in revealing: that when we come clean about the science and what it means, about what would have been and what is needed to keep ourselves and our kin relatively *safe*, about our fears and our grief, about our love for one another and for our children, about what we are determined to do about it, then over time our morale *grows*. Our numbers grow. And, more important, the numbers of the public who are awake to the crisis grow.

The greatest obstacle to the truth being told

I started this chapter by saying that, despite the massive boost that climate-truthfulness has received in the last few years, collectively we are still way off the pace. Far, so far, from really facing up to climate reality.

My claim now is that the greatest obstacle to the truth about climate breakdown being fully told and heard is the fear on the part of so many, still, that if we do so we lose our audience. That fear, I claim, is understandable but ultimately erroneous.

In fact, I'd go further. Unless and until more of us take the plunge of authentically revealing our fears – unabashedly contemplating and exploring the full range of possible future scenarios including the most terrible – and unless and until more of us are willing to face the future without clinging onto rotten crutches such as faith in the COP system, faith in the 1.5°C target as credible, and faith in politics as usual, *then we'll never really get anywhere.*

The only way we get to have a chance of actually responding with sufficient gravity and determination to the insane situation that possesses us, is if we enable the citizenry at large to comprehend that our leaders have failed us, and that even those charged with blowing the whistle on them – journalists, thinktankers, scholars, environmentalists – have mostly not done so. The complicity is wide.

There remains a kind of conspiracy of silence: with 'leading' climate scientists continuing to pretend that what our so-called leaders speak is anything other than the rhetoric of failure. That is, it's a rhetoric that pretends that we are heading to sunny uplands, but whose vacuity is easy to see through. Nearly everyone continues to pretend that we are going to stay below 1.5°C, that we are going to sort this.

But we are not going to simply sort this. Everything is not going to be fine. It is *already* stark-staringly-obviously not fine. And it is going to get worse for a long time to come.

This is what we have collectively to be ready for. That truth needs telling now.

And the telling of it may yet unleash a grief and an anger and a determination that will dwarf the heroic movements of recent years.

A beautiful precedent: Vaclav Havel on living in truth

I take courage, given the immensity of the challenge that I have outlined, from the epochal work of Vaclav Havel, writer, dissident, and last president of Czechoslovakia, especially his great essay 'The power of the powerless'. Havel wrote at a time (the late 70s, in Eastern Europe) when acting on the basis of the truth was punishable by imprisonment. Not so very different as we'd like to imagine from now, perhaps, in the 'West', as our government in the UK moves to criminalise active dissent. He wrote, furthermore, at a time when it seemed impossible to believe that the regimes whose systemic lies he called out could be vulnerable. But he charted a way in which they *were* vulnerable: the power of the powerless is the immense power that comes from telling the truth when the system is *founded* on lies.

The fossil regimes which mostly govern our world, certainly in the UK, might yet prove similarly vulnerable. If only we dare to fully face *our* collective vulnerability now to climate-induced collapse, and to draw the requisite conclusions. And if only, seeing through the founding lies of 'progress', 'endless growth', and so forth, we move decisively beyond the rotten 'leaders' who have led us into this dire quagmire.

Let's turn to Havel's text, to see how he speaks to our condition so directly now. In this excerpt from his great essay, he is seeking to investigate what the 'exit strategy' could be from the crisis of purposelessness. Helpfully for our purposes, he saw this crisis confronting 'Western' countries as much as 'Eastern' countries, only less obviously so. Note especially his unmasking of the hope for a techno-fix or any kind of technocratic 'solutionising' to what is essentially a collective problem of meaning.

> Various thinkers and movements feel that this as yet unknown way out might be most generally characterized as a broad 'existential' revolution: I share this view, and I also share the opinion that a solution cannot be sought in some technological sleight of hand, that is, in some external proposal for change, or in a revolution that is … merely social, merely technological, or even merely political. These are all areas where the consequences of an existential revolution can and must be felt; but their most intrinsic locus can only be human existence in the profoundest sense of the word. It is only from that basis that it can become a generally ethical – and, of course, ultimately a political –reconstitution of society.

> What we call the consumer and industrial (or postindustrial) society … as well as the intellectual, moral, political, and social misery in the world today: all of this is perhaps merely an aspect of the deep crisis in which humanity, dragged helplessly along by the automatism of global technological civilization, finds itself.[66]

I agree, deeply. My appeal to you is to move further toward living in truth: about the desperateness of our plight, and thus about the level, the depth of the response required. Politics is not enough. Activism-as-usual is not enough. What we are dealing with is what Havel called (in Section XVI of his essay) 'a problem of life itself'. The occasion calls for *existential* transformation. All the more so, as we face now a greater threat even than Havel and his compatriots did: literally, an existential threat.

Let's return to what Havel calls, strikingly, 'the most essential matter' of his whole essay… Here is where he *brings home* the direct relevance of his consideration of the power of the powerless to the West, not just to the East; even, he suggests, perhaps more so:

'The post-totalitarian system is only one aspect...of [the] general inability of modern humanity to be the master of its own situation. The automatism of the post-totalitarian system is merely an extreme version of the global automatism of technological civilization. The human failure that it mirrors is only one variant of the general failure of modern humanity.

'This planetary challenge to the position of human beings in the world is, of course, also taking place in the Western world, the only difference being the social and political forms it takes. ...There is no real evidence that Western democracy, that is, democracy of the traditional parliamentary type, can offer solutions that are any more profound. *It may even be said that the more room there is in the Western democracies (compared to our world) for the genuine aims of life, the better the crisis is hidden from people and the more deeply do they become immersed in it.*' (Emphasis added.)[67]

This is why the matter that I have been concerned with is so hard. In the 'West', in the Global North, in actually existing 'liberal democracies', it is hard for us to believe that we are so thoroughly in thrall, so thoroughly unfree. Hard for us to believe that we are not living in the truth that we note (rightly) is routinely, more blatantly denied to the inhabitants of (say) Russia or China. But the obstacle that I have identified in this chapter as perhaps the greatest of all to facing and living in climate-truth, is the very attachment to 'progress', to a 'positive' outcome, to a smooth transition, that is coincident with being captured by the system of thought that rules us. The hegemony of conventional hope. The lie that everything is going to be OK.

Consumer society endlessly tempts us to live within the lie. Many of us don't want to accept that we have already failed to keep ourselves safe, and that any prospect that there once was of a smooth transition has long gone.

But 'I want!' doesn't get. It's time for us to grow up. We should follow the lead that many of our children, magnificently but tragically, have taken since 2018.

The truth I seek to live

What then is the broader truth that we who recognise these painful truths are seeking to live within? It can be summed up swiftly by saying that this civilisation is finished. The breaching of 1.5 is a totem of that larger failure and ending.

The only way we get to come out of this with most of what we love perhaps intact, and certainly with our dignity intact, is if we accept that this civilisation is finished and seek to transform what we have. To create a civilisation that could last.

But this truth is desperately resisted, so desperately that even the desperation is masked, denied.

To be clear, I am not saying that the entire project of civilisation is finished. Rather, that *this* civilisation is finished. The only way we get to come out of this without enduring an uncontrolled civilisational collapse event is by way of paradigm shift, transformative adaptation to another way of living: probably, to a civilisation looking a lot more like an updated form of how indigenous people live – that is, relocalisedly, community-centrically, truly long-term-istically, precautiously – than to how we currently live.

That's why it's too late for anything but radical truth-telling, and acting accordingly.

You, reader, may well not be ready yourself for, say, engaging in civil disobedience. That's completely fine. There are many roles to play, and moderate as well as radical flanks are very much needed in the transformation that is called for. But the entire movement-'ecosystem' needs to be grounded in reality; the reality of the ship of safe seamless transition having sailed, the grim reality that the planet we thought we were living on no longer exists.

And when it is so grounded, and when it is huge enough, the status quo will truly shake.

Together, our great power now rests not in manipulating others to keep the show of activism-as-usual on the road, to keep one's NGO or movement afloat with a production-line of new recruits. Our great power rests, rather, in telling the uncomfortable truth that all of us have failed: yes, this even includes XR and Greta, too. XR's magnificent success in 2019 in changing, perhaps permanently, the conversation around climate (at least in the UK) has not resulted in its demands being met, and there is no chance now of those demands being met by 2025 (which, as I write, is only 1000 days away). The worldwide youth strikes for climate have changed consciousness, but most governments have barely shifted course from growthist business as usual. Greta has been quite explicit that the movement she launched has *not succeeded*: this was the point of her 'blah blah blah' critique at Glasgow at COP26.[68]

Only by facing together that we have barely reached first base on climate, in terms of facing the crisis together, let alone acting adequately on it, do we have any chance of rising at last to this great test of our time.

To the Global South, and to future generations, it is time we spoke up on this: global elites have failed you. The North has let the South down horribly. The older generation has let the younger generation down horribly. These betrayals are not something that any of us from the Global North or from older generations can slough off the taint of. We need to step up to our full humanity if we are to take responsibility for making the best of what comes next.

We now must try to survive what is coming, together.

'Give us more hope!'

In the difficult context just outlined, this really is about whether one has faith in one's fellow humans (and in oneself!) or not. The unwillingness to come clean with one's fellow citizens about just how dire our predicament is, is premised, I have argued, upon the assumption that, if we did come clean in that way, people would be demotivated.

But my experience in the last few years has been the precise opposite. I have found again and again, initially somewhat to my pleasant and profound surprise, that the willingness to tell it like it is, without alarmism or calmism, without optimism (of the intellect) or pessimism (of the will), has been what mobilises most of all. Such authentic truth-telling about the ecological and climate emergency is the key to making headway at this pivotal, terrible, and agential moment in history. A moment, that is, when our agency is called for as never before. A moment from which it is futile to hope for a reprieve by way of leadership from our 'leaders' or by way of tech.

People sometimes say to me, 'But, Rupert, can't you give us more *hope*?' This plaintive question comes from a desire not to have to do the grindingly hard work of staying with the trouble, of being willing to sit for a while with despair and finding our power through that sitting. I would offer two responses to it:

My *first* response to this understandable desire is to say: There are few things that deliver more joy in life than struggling with others for a better future, regardless of outcome: i.e., *regardless of whether* or not we succeed (which it is not in our power to guarantee).

There is nothing more regenerative than authentic campaigning or action for what is needed, when it is done right. I have personally found non-violent direct action *life-changingly* valuable. My experience is that, perhaps surprisingly (given that it seems scary before one has done it), non-violent direct action is highly regenerative and empowering. It's on balance no *sacrifice* to do the right thing, and to know that, whatever happens, at least one truly tried.

There is nothing more rewarding than living in the present, as one exercises one's freedom to speak and act truth to and *as* power, whether at work, where one lives, or on the streets. And, just as Havel ends his essay by suggesting that the attempts by dissidents to live in truth in the Eastern bloc were prefigurative of the better future they sought to co-create, so my experience has been that, in spaces such as Waterloo Bridge or Oxford Circus in the April 2019 Rebellion in London, and in many more inside and outside XR, a better future is already prefigured. That prefiguration is occurring now for instance in the emerging Climate Emergency Centres, and more generally in some of the spaces in the emerging mass moderate flank of the movement. Of course, whilst these examples are inspirational, they are as yet infinitesimally small compared to the heaving behemoth which is business-as-usual society. But the thrilling thing that Havel teaches, and that was seen in Czechoslovakia in 1989, is how the assertion of the truth by a small number can multiply rapidly into a game-changing (r-)evolution.[69]

Just like the awful future we fear, which is already here for many victims of climate disasters, the future we want to live is already here too; only it's very definitely not equally distributed yet, and moreover it is, as yet, only embryonic. But this, though little, is incomparably more than nothing. It could spread almost at the speed of resistance (to what is), of resonance (with what is emerging), of authentic consciousness arising (a phenomenon which this book is a recognition of as well as an intensifier of).

All this is what Havel called 'life in the process of transforming itself'. It will include, crucially, the creation of 'parallel structures' – bottom-up efforts at living in truth. In our case, for instance, transformative adaptation.

My *second* response to the 'Please give us hope' request, which also emerges directly from the argument of this chapter, is to say: Such requests for 'more hope' are in the end misconceived, in any case. For they misconceive *hope itself*. Hope is not really a passive attitude. Hope is, rather, something that one *does*, or even *how* one does it. Hope, properly conceived, is, I venture, more an adverb than a noun.

Active hope is essentially about garnering hope *from the willingness to act*, rather than expecting a psychological attitude of unmoored and often dubiously based desperate hope to produce sufficient action. As my brilliant young friend and colleague Greta Thunberg has so power-fully said: don't ask for hope, rather, hope will spring from action. Start acting and then hope will be everywhere.

So, reader: take action. Whether you believe the specifics of what I have argued in this essay *or not*, just get started, or if you already have started, go further. Take a significant step, whether a 'moderate' or a 'radical' one (there are many to choose from), and *see what happens*. In the world, and in you: in your head, in your heart, and in your soul.

If you need some inspiration, consider the following striking example of a new 'moderate flank' organisation, the smartly named group 'Safe Landing', which aims at one of the hardest of places, the utterly fossil-fixated airline industry, and argues for its reduction and transition. What makes this case so inspiring is that Safe Landing consists entirely of former and serving *airline crew*, including, notably, pilots. These people are ready to take a chance with their own futures for the sake of a common future.

Real active hope is based in faith in ourselves. Faith in our agency. Faith that we really can respond with full adequacy, if we are told the truth in a loving and open way. This is the faith that animates the project of trusting the people, a project manifested in Citizens Assemblies.

So I draw towards conclusion with this bold claim: *we* are the true friends of hope. We who are willing to name the full horror of this historical moment are *thereby* the ones offering and delivering true hope: which is impossible without a willingness to live in the truth. We offer the hope of a sustainable, growing, reality-based movement of movements. Rather than offering manipulation and burnout.

With the continued brave and intelligently targeted efforts from the 'radical' flank, plus millions of activists in the emerging, distributed, mass 'moderate' flank, what occurs *will* be transformative.

Together, we can transformatively adapt to the climate-changed world we inhabit. Terrible hardships and extreme challenges are coming; together, we can face them and find a path through them.

There is no utopia awaiting us at the other end of the journey: the Earth's warming climate and sea level rise, etc., are already fated, due to their anthropogenic destabilisation, to be changing for centuries to come. Together, however, we can *be* the utopia we need, every step of the way. The way forward *is* the path through, the path true: this will be worth calling a utopia of a new kind, a 'thrutopia'.

Faith in ourselves

I believe our best shot now is the radical honesty I have sought to embody in this chapter. There is no chance of any kind of lasting success on a reformed business-as-usual trajectory. This goes for activism as much as it does for society as a whole.

We – rather than those peddling the hopium that events like COP27 are going to get our future sorted – offer the most beneficial active hope. A radical hope: a new hope that can only be born once we have allowed the old, failed hopes to die. A hope, in other words, that *only emerges into view once one has given up the false hopes* of a smooth transition, of staying within 1.5°C.

We have the right to believe that human beings will rise to the challenge of an honest vision.

It is time for us to overcome the greatest obstacle to climate truth: insufficient faith, fellow beautiful humans, in ourselves.[70]

Chapter 11
Climate: This is not an 'emergency'... it's much more serious than that

The original version of this chapter was penned jointly by myself and climate scientist Wolfgang Knorr, and published by Emerge and Perspectiva.[71] The version published here is expanded and updated from that; I take responsibility for the changes. This chapter constitutes, I hope, a deeply uncomfortable intervention. An inconvenient truth, rather than a reassuring lie...

The mantra of 'Climate Emergency!' has been a central feature of the new, exhilarating, and deeply necessary phase of the climate movement that's swept the world since 2018.

This chapter asks an uncomfortable question. What if climate is not really an emergency, but something much *more* difficult? Worse: What if the drive towards declaration of emergency is just another form of immunity to deep change, in disguise?

The main significant practical value of declarations of emergencies by institutions is that the language can be mirrored back to them by activists trying to hold them to account for the next step. But the question asked here is whether that advantage outweighs the significant downside that is here explored.

The contention of this chapter will be that the emergency frame is actually too *optimistic*. It's a form of denial about the width, depth, and tragic nature of the crisis. This will be connected briefly with the contemporary fetish for net zero carbon; both, ultimately, for all their attractions and even successes, are forms of simplistic wishful thinking. Forms even, perhaps, of soft, inadvertent denial.

'Emergency', or what?

Consider the reasonable definition of emergency as either 'an unforeseen combination of circumstances [...] that calls for immediate action', or 'an urgent need for assistance or relief'.[72] We have seen the climate crisis coming for half a century, so the first definition does not apply; what we are experiencing is not 'unforeseen', it is rather a *white* swan. This leaves us with the second, of which *urgency* is the central and indispensable aspect. Urgency is partly an objective notion, referring to what a situation demands. But it is also, and (we suggest) ineradicably, partly a subjective notion, something we feel. It requires us to feel the need for action so strongly that we cannot resist it. If there is, once the situation has been perceived, no genuine *sense* of urgency, then it becomes odd to talk unalloyedly of urgency.

We therefore feel bound to suggest that the subjective aspect of urgency cannot be said to be sufficiently present for it to seem other than odd to call the climate and ecological situation an 'emergency'.

Of course, there remains the arguably not implausible claim that it simply is 'objective truth' that nevertheless this *is* an emergency, that it *is* desperately urgent; *we'll come to that after this section*. But for now, it is time to admit that collectively we humans show, as yet, no behaviour testifying to a sense of irresistible urgency so characteristic of real emergencies, that leave little or no room for second thoughts or prevarication. Collectively, we just do not *feel* that the climate and ecological crisis is an emergency situation. For this *is* partly about what we feel; and it calls into question the widely held view that there is allegedly an action-intention gap at the heart of our reluctance to act. If we do not feel the urgency, it is not credible even to state there is an intention for immediate and radical action. It is not even (just) a matter of courage – that we know deep down what to do but feel somehow unable or unwilling to put this into action. That may be part of it; but, additionally, we – and we mean here very definitely to include climate scientists, activists, etc. – have not grasped the *nature* of the tragic 'problem' of global over-heat and climate chaos. Which is far more than a problem, and whose nature is other than that of a problem.

As many readers will be fully aware, there are growing numbers who have been at least seeking to make the 'emergency' real to us all. Millions of inspiring children, citizens, and activists have in recent years struck a chord; public opinion has changed fairly dramatically in the last few years, now reliably indicating that the broad mass of the population recognise on some level that something is deeply amiss, and are even happy to call it an 'emergency', at least in answering questions put to them by a pollster.[73] This is a remarkable achievement.

But the worry here is that the achievement is not as deep as most activists or scientists desperately hope it to be. It is one thing to get the right answer on an issue-based opinion poll, another to influence actual election results or engage in actual policy – or behaviour – change. Declaring emergency achieves little or nothing in terms of substantive change that the atmosphere will notice and might even, in a twisted way, make us less prone to take the necessary action. The whole drive to declare emergency might give us a sense that we are accomplishing something. When actually we are not coming to grips with the nature of our condition.

What we are faced with is a form of denial, albeit a 'soft' and subtle variant – and a very widespread one indeed. One where we tend to cling on to the false hope that things will turn out to be fine, that we will be saved in some way or other. A perhaps better term is 'disavowal', the systematic burying of painful insights and the avoidance of any attempt to grasp the full scale of the tragic and unbelievable reality. Climate-emergency-talk that spins in the void risks direct complicity with and in fact entrenchment of such disavowal.

There is a dissonance between the increasingly widespread proclaimed emergency-awareness and the ongoing actual lived priorities of individuals, communities, political parties, governments, societies.

One might say that t*he real emergency is precisely that collectively we don't treat this situation as remotely anything like an emergency.* In that sense, the real, paradoxical emergency is that we feel no emergency. In the previous chapter, I called this the 'meta-emergency'. There is a kind of meta-emergency whose core is that we act pretty consistently as if this is not an emergency. So long as that situation persists, then there is something misfiring about regarding what we are living as (simply) an emergency, like the pandemic was. It is at the least so much more layered and difficult and complex than that.

So doubling down and insisting more loudly or shrilly that 'We *are* in a climate emergency!' is too simplistic a way of proceeding at this point. Rather, we ought to recognise the meta-emergency, and examine its nature.

Here is a mini-case-study in the concern that motivates this chapter. Here are the words of an American colleague speaking about his city:

> 'The city of *x* declared a climate emergency last year, as many municipalities have. But last fall the city council agreed to also declare a housing emergency, because the city is woefully short on affordable housing; the city in question is a classic case of a scenic zoom town with a university, good outdoor recreational access, and now in the wake of the pandemic a giant upsurge in immigrants from other cities who are able to relocate in large part because they can work remotely.

> 'Only one city council member objected to the declaration of the housing emergency, on the basis that it cheapened the previous declaration of the climate emergency. So now they are facing both emergencies at the same time. Guess which emergency the city council now spends most of its time discussing? Housing, of course, since it is a matter for now, whereas climate change even in this well-educated community is still seen primarily as a matter for the future. What demarcates the city's progressiveness is that the target date for municipal net zero emissions is 2030 rather than 2050. But this emergency still takes a back seat to more immediate concerns about housing, economic development, and so on.'

Exactly so. Unless and until this becomes about *now*, we're nowhere. And of course, this is desperately hard, in a world where 'more pressing' issues seem ubiquitous: the coronavirus, the 'cost of living', wars, and so forth. Clearly, part of the answer here (as I explored in the closing of *Extinction Rebellion: Insights from the Inside* and in the opening of *Why Climate Breakdown Matters*, with regard to corona, and as I explore further in Chapter 13 below, with regard to Ukraine and the cost of living crisis) is to demonstrate the profound *linkages* and interpenetrations between these 'more pressing' issues and the fundamental underlying ecological and climate realities and ruptures that in truth partly motivate and constitute them. But part of the answer too is what the present chapter seeks to outline. Namely, to set out the crucial respects in which what we are undergoing *vis a vis* climate and ecology is *not* accurately characterised as an 'emergency', *and*, along with the rest of this book, to set out how there *is* an effective way available to alter the temporal focus of our attention to climate etc. That way involves becoming clearly about our (growing) vulnerability *now*, about it's being too late to head off disaster. We are already in it.

Endless fatuous talk of 'keeping 1.5 alive', and of dates like 2030 and 2050, tends to keep us locked in complacent outsourcing of the issue to our 'leaders',[74] in fantasies of an imagined future salvation. It keeps us from actually confronting the situation we are in; and really *acting*.

And, as the following section will investigate, this pickle just cannot be fixed by doubling down on emergency. For there is a real sense in which it cannot be *fixed* at all. The idea of this being a fixable 'problem' is itself a key obstacle to us facing up together to the truth of our condition in this age of climate damage and ecological breakdown. It is not that we ought to try harder to grasp this weird new kind of permanent emergency; it is that the very effort to frame what we are in as an emergency misfires.

The age of stability is over

Does the idea that we have entered the 'Anthropocene' (or the 'Capitalocene', or the 'Chthulucene'…) help us face our reality? In a way, yes. The debate about whether or not we are in the Anthropocene is interesting, but secondary. What is primary is that we are no longer in the Holocene. The age of stability is over. Even in the unlikely event that we manage as a global civilisation to get our act together and act with true grit and determination to rein in the cascading damage that has been unleashed, that damage will go on reverberating down the decades and centuries. For instance, the sea-level rise that we are committed to by virtue of having destabilised the ice sheets.

The comparative coziness and ease of the Holocene, its convenience for agriculture and city-building, is a thing of the past.

The 'emergency' frame is suitable for fierce, *short-lived* matters. In an emergency, it's all hands on deck to *fix* it. But this pickle that we are in is not the kind of thing one fixes.

People can't stay in emergency mode indefinitely, unless, once more, 'emergency mode' means something completely different here to what it normally means. If so, surely it would be better to use a different term. Staying pseudo-permanently in emergency mode is either not really meaning it, as suggested in the previous section, or a recipe for burnout. Staying permanently in emergency mode can't be done; but we *can* potentially shift permanently to a mode of transformative adaptation: of coping with the world that years of inaction have created, of coping with that open-mindedly into a changing future, and of seeking not to add to the damage done.

So the fundamental point in this chapter is: let's admit that the emergency frame isn't capturing all this. Climate and ecological emergency? No. What is emerging *is worse than that*. This is not ever going to get 'fixed'. The 'emergency' frame is too *optimistic*. One might put it thus: it's too *late* for this to be an emergency. (And it's too late partly because it is too slow and long to be an emergency.)

So there is a great letting go to be done here, a great relinquishment. *This* calls for honesty, and spiritual courage.

What we confront is something beyond 'wicked', something truly long-term and structural, and with huge time-lags to boot, something requiring a full-spectrum paradigm shift, not something that can be simply 'fixed' or 'sorted'. We are looking at nothing less than civilisational transformation.

All this points, that is, in the same direction that figures such as Joanna Macy, Duane Elgin, Roy Scranton, Jonathan Franzen, Jem Bendell, Paul Kingsnorth, and Dougald Hine have pointed in. Only unlike the work of some of these authors, the present chapter is determined that this direction not dally with doomism. True, it is time to prepare to fail. It is time for deep adaptation as the ultimate insurance policy against an eco-driven collapse that looms now as the default option.

But it is also, and at the very same moment, time to prepare to succeed, to transform. For if the kind of thing that I (and the likes of Wolfgang Knorr and Marc Lopatin) are saying *lands*, then it is entirely possible that a much larger movement, a much larger wave of action even than the youth climate strikes, could arise. If it really lands with many millions that it's too late for us to picture what we are living as an emergency, that our shared condition is *more serious* than that, then expect a deeper round of eco-grief and climate-anxiety, *and* the action that will emerge from that. Expect a far greater upsurging of love and of rage even than was natal to and expressed through Extinction Rebellion. Expect, after confusion and denial and anomie, the kind of letting go and painful acceptance that we have called for. Expect some congruence between the state our planet is in and our own shared state, at last.

What does 'success' now look like? It looks like that. Not like fixing a problem, but like some shared maturity in action. Crucially, success now looks like a wide, deep, and long rising up whether or not that rising up succeeds in preventing societal collapse.[75] It looks like an emotionally calibrated good-faith upsurge of transformative adaptation. It looks like a larger 'radical' flank, *and* a grand new 'moderate' flank.[76] It looks like millions upon millions 'looking up', really paying attention, waking up, and responding in ways that work for them.

It looks like authentically facing up to climate reality at last; whereas the emergency frame *itself* now looks like a subtle form of denial or disavowal. A subterranean pretence that this 'problem' might get fixed and we could move on. No. What we have entered is a new *condition*.

So it is not an 'objective truth' that this is an emergency. The emergency framing has advantages – and serious disadvantages. It reflects accurately some aspects of our condition – and seriously distorts others.

The 'emergency' disavowal and the 'net zero' disavowal

The net-zero declarations sweeping the world say nothing about what we emit between now and their proclaimed deadlines. They have been *designed* not to require *any* difficult immediate action.

This *seems* very different from – opposite to – the 'climate emergency' declarations sweeping the world. Those are designed to make the situation urgent, to get action to happen now. They seem designed to require immediate action. Right?

But the point that has been being made in this chapter is that the two share something dangerous in common. They are *both* designed to stop us from understanding that we have entered a new basically permanent condition of difficult change and of tragedy. What they have in common is that they are both therefore forms of what I have here called disavowal. The emergency frame, just as much as the net zero frame, subtly delivers the comfort that we can return to the Holocene, that one day the long climate war will be over and maybe we will have won.

That is an illusion that has to be relinquished.

If this matter were raised into public consciousness, and felt-response and reflection and discussion about it ensued, perhaps together it would be possible to find a path not only beyond the deadly distraction of net zero, but beyond the well-meaning but structurally parallel gesture of 'emergency'.

Taking stock

Let us take stock of the point that we have reached.

The normal definition of 'emergency' includes a subjective and an objective aspect.

Subjectively, we do not feel emergency.

This is *itself* a kind of emergency. Given that what we are going through is in some respects a kind of slow-motion version of an asteroid or comet crashing into us, or of an unprecedentedly bad pandemic, or the like, the 'meta-emergency' can plausibly be argued to be the real issue. The real emergency, if there is one, rests exactly in our not feeling our situation to be urgent.

Objectively, however, I have then shown that, while what we are in indeed has *some* things in common with what we usually call 'emergency', on reflection, these are not really enough for us to rest easy with the term. The 'Emergency!' frame subtly disavows the true depth of our travail. In that crucial sense, it itself needs to be disavowed. That gesture, challenging to go through, is what I have been essaying in the previous two sections.

I noted that we need to take stock. *That remark is true of our general situation at this time*, and not merely of your situation at this point in this essay. We need to take stock: we need to take cognisance of the meta-emergency, and we need to dwell in particular in the sense of how the situation we are in is *more than* a 'mere' emergency, more than something fixable, more than something that will ever end for us, more than a challenge to our ingenuity; rather, a challenge to our entire mode of existence, a challenge to our very selves. A civilisational challenge, a necessary questioning of our very paradigm.

What emerges from genuinely taking stock is what could *move* us to more or less voluntary transformative change. (Without which, most of what we know and love will be swept away anyway.)

In the final section of this chapter, I seek to enter deeper into such emergent stock-taking.

What lies beyond 'emergency'

It might well be that in some contexts there is no politically expedient short-term alternative but to milk out of the 'climate emergency' frame whatever we can. What this chapter has been doing is raising awkward questions, that so many want to avoid, about what some call the 'meta-crisis' (that I examine at greater length in Chapter 13). About how this crisis is much bigger than something fixable, bigger, longer, deeper even than a 'wicked' problem. About why, therefore, the emergency frame for climate felt game-changing but is actually, at the end of the day, desperately ill-fitting.

At the end of the day it's of course not up to any individual to decide whether this be called an emergency or not. But *if* this is (called) an 'emergency', the key point in this chapter has been that it is of an utterly different nature to what we are used to calling 'emergency'. It is a super-long-run 'emergency'. It is a novel, more or less permanent condition. It is tragic; our drowning in it has to do with deep civilisational flaws, with a wide and over-determined hubris.

Above all, it is unlike anything we have ever called an emergency before. It is not even very much like Nazism / the Second World War, in ways that are pretty obvious: there is no properly 'external' enemy; there is not going to be any fixing it and returning to 'normal'. We are launched on a path literally into *terra incognita*, a new Earth.[77] The new normal is climate instability; the new normal is no new normal. Rather it is change, including chaos. (In this way, the anodyne, weak, sleep-inducing, widest-used term for our predicament, 'climate change', perhaps inadvertently points to a truth. What has changed is not 'merely' the climate; what has changed is whether we can any longer reasonably hope not to be living in a world that is (drastically and challengingly and constantly) changing. What we have done to our climate is to force, for the first time, a negative answer to that implied question.)

The suggestion of this chapter has been that the best response to this situation, on balance, is to let go of the emergency frame. One could say that that the situation we have entered is not an emergency, but rather a call for us collectively to come to our senses and value life as it is and has been and still could be. A call to let go of the aspiration of civilisational superiority; a call for wisdom and humility.

So not something complicated like a 'wicked problem', but something both conceptually simple *and* difficult (letting go). It is what Wittgenstein was talking about when he said that the real issue is not problems of the intellect but of the will. *Are we willing to face the awful present, and the changing future; and are we ready to will what needs to be done?* It's not about cleverness, nor even about urgency; it's about integrity.

There is of course a sense in which this has *always* been the (more-than-)problem: am I/are we willing to confront the awful and largely – or at least partly – avoidable suffering that's going on right now among billions of living beings (human and otherwise), and has been going on for as long as beings capable of suffering have existed? And even if I were/am capable of facing this truth, what would/will I do with it? Climate is just another variant of the basic problem of being a caring human being: how can I possibly face the incredible suffering of others (and perhaps of myself), and how do I get into the place I need to be in, the place where I can imagine that I – together with others – can do something meaningful about it. The *difference* is that the issue now is one of incalculably ramped-up scale and consequence. People sometimes say to me: But Rupert, for many people, collapse is already happening. I respond to them: If you think this is already collapse, be careful…because you ain't seen nothin' yet.

What we are at is a point of no return, a climax, already partly passed. And (t)here's a call – a chance – to realise that. A choice to value what we have left, however much or little that is, and then embrace it together without indulging the limitations of the catastrophic culture that has brought us to this pass.

Either there will be a paradigmatic shift of that nature, or we will cling onto the fantasy of universal mastery and go down with it.

This philosophical choice is not of the nature of an emergency.[78] It's far more important than that. It cuts way deeper than that.

Chapter 12
Will the passing of 1.5 degrees see the end of cruel optimism? Telling the whole truth at five past midnight

This chapter follows up on the previous two, in that it aspires to expound the story-change required if we are to make progress in a way that shriller calls for action cannot. And it emphasises how the needful change here begins at home. That is, it's about 'us', inside the climate 'bubble', being willing to speak and act as if it's five past *midnight. Until we do, no one else will.*

The original version of this chapter was penned jointly with Marc Lopatin (comms-adviser to Jeremy Corbyn in the 2017 general election campaign, and a key player in the 'moderate flank' *initiative) for Resilience.[79] It has been lightly edited for this book.*

'The public gets what the public wants' sang a young Paul Weller on the 1979 hit *Going Underground*. There's a sense in which that lyric doubles as a one-line summary of the 2022 IPCC report by the world's leading climate scientists. For all that the report is stark, and contains much that is exciting, important, and new, there's a sense in which it continues to tell an old, old story.

In the second installment of its Sixth Assessment Report, the Intergovernmental Panel on Climate Change (IPPC) thundered that it's 'Now or never' to stave off climate disaster. Yet when it came to how the world might respond, the same IPCC authors were prevented from giving anything like equal voice as to why previous warnings have gone unheeded. In the politically charged process of producing the report's summary, all mentions of 'vested interests' (the fossil fuel industry and others invested in a high-carbon economy) were removed, while Saudi Arabia, one of the world's largest oil producers and exporters, successfully argued for the inclusion of multiple references to Carbon Capture and Storage (CCS).

Even what should be understood as the wider report's main finding – the impossibility in practice, the utter implausibility now, of restricting global average temperature rise to the 'safe' threshold 1.5°C – was left to the most alert portions of the commentating media and to scientists outside of the IPCC process to highlight. The IPCC for its part stated that without 'deep and immediate' cuts in emissions across the globe, there would be less than even a 33% chance of staying below 1.5°C. They subsequently clarified that 'immediate' means this year, 2022. And that's *worldwide*, folks. Is it really responsible to present this chance as if it is even remotely plausible?

The effectively inevitable breaching of a globally agreed planetary boundary for averting dangerous climate change has thus far failed to cut through. The coverage of the recent IPCC reports has used grave and scary language, but a loophole in public consciousness is always left open. It is implied or asserted that we still have time in theory to stay safe.

The failure of the latest report to stay in the headlines for long enough to enable the unearthing of its buried implication – that actually staying below 1.5°C is, for those of us in the reality-based community, in practice dead[80] – was partly due to timing. There is a war involving a 'great' (sic) power going on in Europe for virtually the first time since World War II, and at the time of the report's publication, mainstream news outlets were reporting alleged war crimes by retreating Russian troops in Ukraine.

But it is doubtful that the IPCC's latest installment would have been big news anyway. This is for two reasons. Firstly, most of the immediate victims of a '1.5°C+ world' are not living in high wage economies across the Global North. They are living at the other end of international supply chains across the Global South. Even by the IPCC's own (probably conservative) reckoning, unprecedented numbers of people living in vulnerable countries will be exposed to food insecurity, flooding, and displacement unless action is taken.

The second reason for the muted public reception relates to the first: the IPCC advanced what could be termed a get-out-of-jail-free card for those of us living across the Global North. It's called 'overshoot' and can be found in scientific modelling of Earth's climate that shows average temperature going above 1.5°C for a period of decades, before supposedly falling back down beneath. Such modelling is premised on the widespread and efficient post-2050 deployment of yet to be invented Carbon Dioxide Removal (CDR) technologies, to suck massive amounts of carbon out of the atmosphere to cool the earth back to below 1.5°C. The illusion they are selling is that we can stay below 1.5 degrees *by way of going above it*, by 'overshooting' and then, allegedly, returning to where we need to be.

Our point here is not only that 'overshoot [and return]' won't work – because of irreversible harms and because of tipping points that set off further dynamics that can't just be reversed even if we do get back below 1.5 – but that, partly because of those tipping points, it is very unlikely that we will get back below 1.5 if (i.e., when) we go above it. That is devastating enough. Our immediate point is that it is Orwellian in the worst sense to pretend that going above 1.5°C is a way of staying below 1.5°C. It is a way of trying to get your audience to remain calm, to not notice when something terrible has happened. To not notice the culprits. To not notice that we are out of the safe zone.

There really couldn't be a better way for the IPCC – inadvertently or otherwise – to reinforce the story that the public wants: *that climate disaster is still way off, lots of good stuff is happening now to stop it, and there are solutions on the horizon to take up the slack for what we can't do today*. It's why saying it's 'now or never' to stave off climate disaster packs no emotional punch. Overshoot cancels out the warning since it offers a concerned public the permission to stay passive. Overshoot is, if you will, a form of imagined salvation. As a means of sustaining inaction in the now, tomorrow's whiz-bang CDR tech could even be framed as the natural heir to yesteryear's climate denial.

So while the IPCC's mainstreaming of overshoot has provided a 'bit of a boost' to the carbon removal industry, it has more importantly laid the foundation for the public to perceive overshoot as 'good science'. While there is the merest promise of a technical fix, tomorrow never comes. The clock never runs down. This is how imagined salvation works: it literally freezes our reaction time to dangerous climate change at five to midnight.

Even a casual consumer of climate politics and campaigns will know it's been five to midnight for decades. Overwhelmingly and under-standably, few of us want to make drastic consumer changes in the here and now on the promise of making life bearable for our unborn (and born!) grandchildren. It is why the climate story as told is built around *#YesWeCan*, whether it's Big Oil promising to go 'net zero' *or* their detractors blocking UK refineries calling for an end to all new oil exploration licences and tacitly or explicitly claiming that they can save us from nemesis within the next three or so years.

#YesWeCan is, perhaps surprisingly, a story that tends to happen around us as opposed to *with* us. On the high-tech version of it: The world that we know will essentially be safeguarded by CDR and non-fossil energy generation while heat pumps, electric cars, and even lab-grown meat will be *de rigeur*. In other words, we and our operating system will essentially be left intact. No need to reassess who we are and our place in the world.

Therein lies the imagined salvation that we can all carry on with the system we have, merely powered with different energy sources. It was never very credible; it is now altogether absurd. And yet it is only very slowly breaking down. But why so slow? Well, aside from Big Oil's de-cades-long assault on climate science, it's also because Big Oil's main *opponents* – scientists, environmental campaigners and even many of the most hardcore of activists – are loathe (alongside mainstream media) to tell the public a different story. The perceived fear of losing the public to despair and apathy, not to mention the professional risk of breaking ranks, are deemed too high.

But in repeatedly giving the public the story it wants, there is paradoxically no participatory audience to lose. 'Five to midnight' is permission to stay passive. To keep outsourcing concern to those fighting the good fight in the somewhat elitist climate 'bubble' of engaged activists, scientists, etc. There's no widespread deep and emotional connection with climate and ecology. Concern about climate is now widespread in the UK, but it is shallow.

People are not coming together en masse to act collectively in the face of existential risk. And there is an argument that the knee-jerk doomism that drips casually from peoples' lips at the mere mention of climate might itself be a symptom of being repeatedly exposed to a compulsory but evermore implausible *#YesWeCan* after every news item telling of accelerated ice-melt and unmodelled extreme weather. Even when imagined salvation backfires it still results in passivity. Almost genius really.

All this helps explain why waiting for the IPCC to finally (and messily) call time on 1.5°C has cost humanity more reaction time. Worse still, most individual scientists and virtually the whole of civil society have in effect surrendered 1.5°C's passing to a politically overseen body (the IPCC) that has not only soft-pedalled its passing but has added insult to injury by legitimising dangerous 'overshoot'[81] of 1.5° (and probably, in due course, of 2°, too) in a bid to placate an audience. An audience that, because of the endless soft-pedalling and 'hopium'-peddling, is barely there.

One would therefore like to think that the passing of 1.5°C into history's rear-view mirror should give profound pause for thought. Not least because of the spectre of abandonment that now hangs over the Global South for all to see. The climate injustice here is absolutely stark.

If you believe in climate justice – that is, justice for the Global South and for future generations on the critical question of our time – then the best thing to do is not to shout louder that we must keep 1.5 alive: doing that is merely playing Conservative climate boss Alok Sharma's game. The best thing to do, instead, is to point out, with all due realism and horror, the betrayal.

The alternative is to massage away 1.5°C as 'always impossible' and double down with the same old story and tactics to meet the Paris Agreement backstop of 'well below 2 degrees'.

The point of this chapter is not to say that highlighting a missed political goal will suddenly make a properly emotive crisis out of a (more-than-)wicked 'problem'. But surely one can harbour hope that this moment could at least encourage those in the climate 'bubble' – the elite of 'policy-makers'/scientists/activists – to ask themselves, and each other, some *existential questions* to sit alongside the oft-cited existential risks of climate breakdown. Chief among those questions is whether continuing to fight for 1.5°C after the point where it was plausible may have negatively impacted the UK public's willingness to seek to move beyond merely *imaginary* salvation.

Are scientists, campaigners, and activists willing to elevate truth telling and risk disrupting imagined salvation to at least make it harder for the public to outsource their passive concern to those active in the bubble? How, in particular, will climate justice activists respond to the 'age of over-shoot'? Will they choose to express grief at what cannot be saved, and rage at the betrayal, and thus mobilise on the basis of the power of truth? Or will they just keep playing basically the same game as those scientists, politicians, and businesspeople who are all still locked into hoping or pretending that somehow we are going to make everything OK?

From a straightforward storytelling perspective, there is opportunity. Climate decline is no longer 100% future focused. Paradoxically, it now has a 'future past' as 1.5°C will now come no matter what mitigation successes follow. It is as if the climate story has finally left the spirit world and taken bodily form, a little like Lord Voldemort in the Harry Potter novels.

What those of us in the bubble will do in response is uncertain. Back in 1979, Paul Weller's riposte was to turn away and go underground. In 2022 and beyond, we need to do the opposite: trust the public, bring people together, and let the story in. The true story.

When that process accelerates, when the momentous realisation that we are definitively out of the safe zone takes hold, it will mark the beginning of the immediate *and* long-term fight for our lives.

Chapter 13
Ukraine, our failed operating system, and a climate-realist future to live for

The 'full-on' response to our most current of crises that I essay here, like the Introduction and Conclusion, was penned especially for this book. It draws together themes from the last few chapters, and thus prepares the ground for (as it were) achieving exit velocity from the book. For it suggests that we will not get very far if we only seek to turn the Ukraine crisis and the cost of living crisis it has spawned into a 'five to midnight' moment, a 'last chance' to do the right thing at last on climate and energy. (And that instead what is needed is the kind of grittier and yet bolder truth-based organising set out in more detail in the Conclusion, as envisioned especially under the broad heading of the emerging new 'moderate flank'.)

We should have transitioned our economies and societies off fossil energy a decade ago. *Two*, even three decades ago. We should have pivoted away from these finite and dangerous energy sources, from the system of the past, long before Vladimir Putin put his vicious oar in and tried to hold us all to ransom. We should at the very latest have done so when offered the vast opportunity that was the COVID-19 crisis.

But we didn't.

We didn't do it then; the next best time to do it is right now, under pressure. The International Energy Agency is offering a 10 point plan to dramatically reduce demand for oil; a number of European countries (led from the EU) have created impressive initiatives of various kinds to decarbonise.

Might we then do it this time? Might this be the moment when we get climate-savvy, with a gun pointed at our heads? Well, it should be.

But it won't be. At least, we won't decarbonise *enough*, let alone fast enough. That is already obvious from the responses of countries like the UK and the USA, which, as well as doubling down on selected renewables, are tripling down across the board on 'home-grown' fossil fuels too.

Our situation in the UK is, at time of writing,[82] particularly nauseating. The government now in power is 'led' by Liz Truss, a terminal lightweight, whose main qualification for being prime minister appears to be her rigid ideological closeness to fossil fuel interests and her opposition to redistribution. This government is arguably the worst government we have ever had, certainly on climate and nature. Jacob Rees-Mogg, senior Cabinet minister now for business, energy, and the environment, is close to being a climate denier. The new government plans to frack the UK, despite the very poor prospects for doing so yielding very much usable energy, and despite the fact that fracking this country will do nothing to reduce energy bills here, because we are part of an international market in fossil fuels. Jacob Rees-Mogg is determined to drill 'every last drop' of oil out of the North Sea. And to cap it all, they are green-lighting the opening of a new coal mine in northern England.

That such a government is in power, at this moment in history, and even in the wake of the encouraging positive shifting public attitudes on climate that we've noted in earlier chapters, is a stupendously depressing wake-up call.

In quite a number of countries, including the UK, the terrible, insane truth is that it would appear that we are not even decarbonising anymore. We have started heading in the wrong direction. The response to Russia's international aggression, climate- and energy-wise, in countries like the UK, has headed in the wrong direction.

It's heartbreaking, it's stupid, it's infuriating. It's understandable (in the context of extreme short-termism and narrowness of vision, and of vast vested interests). In any case: it's true.

Don't get me wrong; it's not of course as if we have any *excuse* for not doing the right and necessary – transformational – thing without delay. Who knew that we could willingly lockdown entire societies, that is, lockdown *ourselves*? Who knew that we could furlough and support tens of millions of people? The collective response to COVID-19 proved that all the things that have been said about why acting now, adequately, on the climate more-than-emergency, is allegedly impossible, are false. (Especially, the truly precautious response to COVID-19 in countries like New Zealand, Taiwan, South Korea, and some West African countries: countries that responded far more adequately than the UK or the USA, and suffered far less death, *and far less economic disruption in total*, as a result.[83])

And yet, it isn't happening, not even in countries (like Germany) which are sort-of trying, under the severest of pressure from Putin's strategy of fossil-energy-withholding.

The latest IPCC report from Working Group II (on vulnerability, adaptation, and resilience), for which I was one among dozens of expert reviewers – perhaps the starkest IPCC report yet – warns in its culminating line that 'any further delay in concerted global action will miss a brief and rapidly closing window to secure a liveable future'. Guess what: drilling for more fossil energy (as is happening especially in the UK and the USA at great scale) is nothing if not further delay, and worse. The latest IPCC report from Working Group III, on mitigation – the best (sic) yet – has called, as previous chapters noted, for rapid, deep, and immediate cuts in greenhouse gas emissions, worldwide. Such cuts, it makes clear, need to kick off this year, 2022: – that is the meaning of 'immediate'. But look around the world and this shared will simply is not visible.

The window is shut.

We are not pivoting now, nowhere near enough. Because, if one takes a global overview, we are pivoting away from the past *and* towards it – towards more fossil-fuelled death – at the same time!

This is happening because more immediate emergencies always take precedence over the climate and ecological perma-'emergency', this endless less-and-more-than-emergency. Less in that it feels less urgent. More in that, as I laid out two chapters ago, it is (partly therefore) more intractable than 'mere' emergencies.

It's happening because so long as we continue to imagine that we have time, that climate catastrophe is something for later, then we never act on it at sufficient speed and scale.

What we need to do is shift to understanding that the catastrophe is here.

What do I mean by that?

First, I mean that it's all one joined up thing: petro-dictators, oligarchs, a mostly useless mass media, chronic short-termism, a harsh 'cost-of-living' crisis (which is indistinguishable from an inequality crisis), *epochal* inequality, despoliation of the natural world. It's all connected. It's one joined-up, screwed operating system.

The Ukraine invasion is a symptom of a global civilisation that is fin-ished. But such a civilisation has forms of denial built in. And is particu-larly hard to rouse, having become so polarised. There isn't going to be any quick-win awakening from this nightmare. We can hope that this is the moment of the decisive pivot. We will be hoping in vain.

And second, I mean that we've already locked in a good deal of the ca-tastrophe. Because of the inertia built into both the climate and human systems, it's already in effect roughly 2032…

The only way we get to get beyond the path-dependency we are living, the only way we get to find a way out of this *stuckness*, the only way we get to get beyond the failed system that is consuming our future in real time, is if we recognise how deep the malaise is; if enough of us, based thus in truth, demand a different paradigm; if we accept that the pious hopes of a smooth transition to a future with a liveable climate are dead. The window to smoothly transition beyond fossil fuels is shut. There isn't going to be a smooth transition; we are not going to stay within 1.5 degrees of over-heat; *this* civilisation is not going to save itself.

We get through this now and henceforth in some kind of tolerable, perhaps even compassionate adaptation only if we let go of those fantasies that I've just listed in the previous paragraph. Because doing so returns us to reality, where we can stand, where we can do no other. The anger and despair and grief at realising how very much we have already committed to destruction already can rocket-power us. What has been seen to date, in the likes of XR and the youth climate strikes, is only the beginning. It proves the power of authentic truth-telling, of unabashed love for our living world and our kids and ourselves. But there is far, far more where that came from.

Even XR has tended to be, if anything, too caught up in the system as-is. XR's demands were an attempt at a quick fix. That is not, it is now clear, the way transformative change is going to happen. It is going to proceed slowly, or in fits and starts, for a while longer, as people painfully wake up to the fact that it is not going to happen as it 'should' happen (smoothly, determinedly, early) and then get serious about (transformative) adaptation, about system-change, about a new paradigm. It can speed up once we get critical mass; but that is, frustratingly, going to take a while.

I can hear some readers getting frustrated right now: 'But we don't have that time!!' You're right, we don't. We're *already* too late – for any kind of vaguely serene transition. So buckle up. And *turn* that frustration – which will continue for a long time! – into energy that is available for the great work we have to do…

I have felt that frustration that you may be feeling, so much. Like I say: we should have pivoted a decade or more ago. But we didn't. Because the system is f***ed. And until we acknowledge that, we will effect only superficial change.

Those who go on pretending that we can still do this without great harm accruing to many of us, pretending that the COP system is viable, pretending that the window is still open, pretending that 1.5 degrees is still practicable as an upper limit to overheat, pretending that we can mitigate our way out of this, pretending that tech-fixes and technocracy are up to the job ... remain part of the problem. Those who endlessly maintain that it's five minutes to midnight (or one minute to, or half a minute to) have a lot of responsibility for the rise in outright doomerism, especially among the young. For these pretences are *not credible*. They lead only to disappointment, burnout, and a form of despair that sticks.

I have heard it said (in private) by very senior figures in the g/Green movement that we should keep the aspiration for 1.5 degrees alive for 'completely convincing tactical reasons'. I take it this means things like: We aim for 1.5 and prepare for 2–4. Or: 1.5 is a negotiating technique. Or: we keep 1.5 to 'keep hope alive' among citizens, or among small island states; etc. Or something like that. But these are all prettified ways of saying that we are not levelling with people about how utterly, completely improbable 1.5 now is, about how there is zero sign of seriousness in aiming at it, about how the fixation on 1.5 prevents us taking transformative adaptation let alone deep adaptation at all seriously, and about how increasingly an air of unreality permeates the entire discourse and threatens to poison it.

That is the politics of euphemism, the politics of pretence. It is the politics, perhaps worse still, of prevarication. It is losing us response-time at a time when we do indeed need to move as fast as we are able (while realising, with the realism we always need, that it won't be fast enough to preserve the hopes we had had).

With each passing day, as the reality hardens around and against us, we risk sounding less and less like we are interested in telling the truth, the more we cling to the not-going-to-be-attained goal of 1.5°C. By concentrating all attention on the ever-narrowing, ever-more-minute, ever-more-fantastical window of opportunity for 1.5, we remove attention from what *is* still possible, and so necessary, and set ourselves up for dreadful discourses of 'overshoot'. (As mentioned in Chapter 12, there will soon be widespread pretence that we can hit 1.5 by missing it!?!: by going over it and allegedly coming back under it later by way of green house gas-removal tech.) We set ourselves up for mass burnout (of climate activists).

I understand that there is great grief around letting go of 1.5. But we need that grief. As I've outlined in previous chapters, that grief is what will rocket-power us.

Letting go of 1.5 would – will – require a massive, heart-stopping admission of failure and a sobering facing up to reality. That is the main reason why people don't want to do it. My take, as set out in earlier chapters: an admission of failure *is precisely what we need*.

Saying that there are 'completely convincing tactical reasons' for keeping 1.5 alive is saying, we are going to lie to people, to try to string them along in a spirit of 'positivity', awhile longer. It is a recipe for – an endorsement of – deceit and betrayal.

But the dream of 1.5 is dying only slowly, inside the climate bubble. The long march of climate-realism will be utterly, frustratingly slow, at least for a while longer. This even has its advantages: it provides time to reflect, and such reflection is much needed. It provides time to strategise and build. In my view, the movement (of movements) we need above all to build, the forms of action we so need to foster, will aim at truly mass involvement, will be genuinely inclusive, will be realistic about what can be expected of governments in the short term (i.e., not a great deal), will attempt to build the alternative system from ground up, and will be sanguine about the terrible pain that will be endured from our having left things so absurdly late.

So, the message of those of us engaged in this long march, and determined not to relapse into Pollyanna-ism, needs to be: we're ready to greet you. We're ready and eager to welcome the many millions who are going to stumble heartbroken into this space in the coming years. That includes being ready to receive ex-doomers when you've spent enough time stuck in despair, and the ex-stubborn-optimists when you get it that endless stubbornness at some point ceases being a virtue, and that putting on a happy face in the face of disasters is not the way to go. Let us know when you are ready for *us*. We're here. And we're ready to offer support and solidarity.

Spiritual and wisdom traditions have long practiced an alternative to the culture of instant gratification. They will remain after it has died out, along with *this* civilisation. That culture infects even the most scintillating of activist responses to the current cataclysm, such as XR.

But: the tortoise always wins. We just don't know whether it/we will win in time to prevent collapse, and the 'harvest' of mass death that it would bring. But that is not in the end ours to determine. It is a painful gift to be alive in these times of heartbreak and of vast transformative opportunity. But it is a *gift*, nevertheless. In the end, we have no choice but to embrace the gift, and strive for a future to live for, a future even that could yet be one of flourishing, in a saner imaginary and a more civil civilisation. A future that would be *to die for*.

For all we have to do, whenever we live, is decide what to do with the time that is given us. A time that is always 'too short', but that is most certainly long enough for us to get real in.

Conclusion
Mourn, *and* organize: Proposals for how to implement the truth-telling agenda most effectively

'True words aren't charming. Charming words aren't true.'

– From the Dao De Jing

Recall the story I told in the Preface to this book of the bloke who asked my sister, 'Do you want to know the truth?'

This man, who was selling my sister a rabbit, was tempted not to tell her the truth; he feared that if he told her the truth she wouldn't purchase the rabbit. We sometimes don't want to tell the truth for self-interested reasons. But what this book has sought to show is that it's not only that we ought, regardless of consequences, to break this habit and, in the words of XR's epochal first demand, 'Tell the truth', but that it is *always* – on balance, in time – *best* to be willing to know the truth, to hear the truth. Even when, and in fact *especially* when, doing so is painful.

That is what this book is about. In this conclusory chapter, I will seek to draw together some lessons from the truth about truthlessness and truthfulness, by way chiefly of drawing out what I believe *should come next in terms of 'the climate movement'* and climate/nature action more generally.

The body of this book has mainly consisted in a diagnosis of our ills, and a prognostic cure: levelling with each other. We need people to break cover. Whenever someone with any insider knowledge of the system retires, they should tell all. Better still, scientists and politicians and regulators and fiduciaries and insurers and many many more should break cover *now*: disclose, or whistleblow, or become 'double-agents'.

And in fact all of us can contribute by at minimum emotionally disclosing. Every parent, every teacher, *everyone* who tells the world of their fears, their grief, their anger, and their love is a nail in the coffin of the collapse-trajectory of this future-eating civilisation.

But I haven't said as much as some readers might want, in the main body of the book, about *how to organise* to accomplish the goal of truth-telling-based climate action and build on it. Various chapters have touched on this theme in various ways, and sometimes I have dwelt too on the inevitable resistance to this vivacious virus of truth: for instance, in Chapter 6, in the context of GreensCAN, I faced and thought through the way that a bridling and bristling against a politics of truth-telling is to be expected; and is ultimately further grist to the mill. If there weren't resistance, we would know that we're not scratching the right itch.

My hope is that the trajectory of my thinking in this book will help midwife the emergence of a resurgent and much larger movement, based thoroughly in these difficult truths that the chapters in the main body of this book have dwelt on. Let me turn now full-bloodedly to that task: to asking explicitly what the logic of living in truth implies for what ought to come next. If we seek to live in truth, just what will the movement and action that comes now on climate look like?

Part of my answer can be found in pondering the wonderful old labour-movement slogan, 'Don't mourn, *organise*', which I suggest needs updating – in fact, overturning! – for our time. We need to face reality, and that *requires* us to mourn. If we didn't feel profound grief for what is, for what is lost, and in relation to much of what is coming, we wouldn't be human, we wouldn't be facing authentically up to our time. The consequence of such mourning, *provided* it is given a context of agency, empowerment, and/or of viable ways to act, is an imperative to organise. Effectively. To achieve what can still be achieved. Which is less than some make out: we can't magic our way out of the consequences of the decades of destruction and inaction. And yet, *simultaneously*, what can still be achieved is far *more* than is even dreamt of by most: when we face the truth, and allow ourselves to meet it fully in our humanity and animality, as emotionally-real Earthlings, such things become possible as dreams are made of. We have only begun, in the last four years or so, to tap this great power. This Conclusion investigates how we might tap it far, far more.

What now, on climate and ecology?

Let's start with the obvious and unpalatable. One implication of the analysis contained in the main body of this book is that we must make ready for potential civilisational collapse. We haven't prevented the existential threat ever so slowly rearing up before us. We haven't mitigated the threat adequately. We have failed to adequately prepare. Therefore, we must prepare to fail. Adequately, decently, as ethically as possible; perhaps even beautifully. That is an encapsulation of what deep adaptation *is*.

For we must actually *prepare*. Not just talk about preparing, but initiate preparedness, psycho-spiritually *and* materially. We must dare to enter in our minds and our hearts into the space of potential collapse. And we must ready our agriculture, and all our systems, against and in the light of that potentiality.

But let us do so not shying away from the power that can be unleashed by active hope, as we so prepare, as we look into the abyss. An anecdote: I visited Poland in 1987, as part of a group seeking to engage with dissidents there. Poland was at the time under long martial law. We were followed and routinely (albeit softly) intimidated by the secret police of the Communist regime. We undertook the first video-interview with Lech Walesa (then head of the banned Solidarity trades union) since martial law had been declared, and we smuggled it out of the country in an embassy bag.

I had a remarkable experience, there in Gdansk. Encountering citizens protesting even under martial law, singing pro-Solidarity songs, attending 'politicised' church services (the Church being one of the few places where any organising was still possible), I found myself coming to an extraordinary, seemingly absurd conclusion. Without understanding how it was possible, I became convinced that these people would win. I went back to Britain and told a number of people of my conviction. They'd typically ask me, 'But how? How are they possibly going to win, against an implacable authoritarian regime?' I had no sensical answer. None at all. All I knew was that I somehow knew that they were going to win. That their spirit, their living in truth, would see them through to success. I somehow knew that their authenticity, the truth that they were still living in the face of the lie of total state control and an unchangeable system, had itself an implacable power. Slower, but surer, than the harder but shallower power of the oppressors.

It turned out that, two years later, the dissidents indeed achieved their victory. In the dark times we are living, we need remembrances like that. We need allies/gurus like Vaclav Havel (who I honoured in Chapter 10), the greatest theorist of all this. We need to live in truth, and then extraordinary, 'impossible' things, like (more recently) the Arab Spring, or indeed the 2019 April Extinction Rebellion, can occur.

Havel and his ilk get praised by the political Right, as resisters to Communism, as civilisational dissidents. But the incredibly striking thing about Havel's essay 'The power of the powerless' when one actually *reads* it, as I sought briefly to illustrate in my chapter, is that it is in fact a general critique of techno-industrial modernity and of the crisis of meaning inherent in the consumerism and atomism it produces.

It is that system, most especially in its capitalist forms, which now requires dissidents. Dissent. That is an inconvenient truth that the Right (and most of the actual-existing 'Left'!) ignore.

We need to know that – as occurred in Poland in 1989 – what seems impossible can become possible, and then even commonsensical, unavoidable: through telling and living in the truth.

Only then can something emerge which will stop us from heading ever deeper into a worse-than-emergency.

But the challenge facing us is, as I've set out elsewhere, considerably harder than the challenge faced by the East European dissidents, or by the civil rights movement, or by the Suffragettes.

So, I suggest that part of the purport of deep adaptation, which *means* adaptation to potential collapse, is to be a 'mind-bomb', forcing into unwilling consciousnesses that this is for real: we mean it, collapse is now all-too-possible, in fact all-too-probable. Probably not immediate nor even soon, at least in richer or more climate-stable parts of the world. But visible. A more-than-horizonal potential. To stop it will now demand extraordinary heroism and innovativeness.

As I see it, deep adaptation by no means constitutes or legitimates us giving up on trying to *prevent* climate(-induced) collapse, but it is a reasonable and necessary philosophical and practical exercise to undergo when we are honest with ourselves about the pretty desperate situation we are in. In other words, one of the reasons for thinking potential collapse is so that we can be better prepared for it in psychological *and* practical terms if and as it starts to unfold.

At time of writing, adaptation is still being taken nowhere near as seriously as 'mitigation'/prevention in climate-politics. Why? One reason is because once we start talking about or even doing adaptation, *we can no longer deny how bad the situation is*. And that is what most people are still uncomfortable doing. This failure to engage seriously with adaptation, let alone deep adaptation, risks being a form of tacit/soft climate denial in action. And it is losing us precious time.

It's (high) time to prepare for the worst. That's so especially because there is not enough preparedness for the worst being undertaken; and that absence of course increases our vulnerability further. This is the meta-emergency. And similarly, it's simply because if we don't prepare for the worst, then we will get burnt the worst if/when it comes. I'm not giving up on the fight to stop our society undermining its own future existence; far from it. On the contrary, when I contemplate the likelihood of collapse, and the need therefore for deep adaptation, it makes me all the more determined to try to *stop* collapse, even if the chances of succeeding in doing so seem so very slim. But *not* being willing to be honest enough to contemplate it isn't going to help us. On the contrary. As the collapsologists put it in the book *Deep Adaptation* that Jem Bendell and I co-edited: only staring collapse in the face as if it is coming right for us has the power to jolt us into doing enough about it to stop it mowing us down.

We more or less *know* what we need to do. This has not been a book about the content of that knowledge (others have written on that at length, usually with much more verve or expertise than I). And in any case, as I say, we all more or less know the basic outlines by now: we need to get off (our addiction to) fossil fuels, we need to end our addiction to 'economic growth', we need to transition the runaway food system into something saner and kinder, and we need a massive programme of retrofit for buildings; more generally, we need to tread much more lightly on the Earth, to genuinely resilientise, to relocalise, and to start observing the Precautionary Principle more than just in the breach. The crucial thing, the thing that is missing, is to *acknowledge* this knowledge, to dare to inhabit what we know, and to turn more earnestly to implementing it. Not being put off by the thought that such a system-change is daunting and ought really to be led from the front by our 'leaders'. As I've argued in this book, it is much too late in the night to allow that thought, true enough though it is, to put us off from acting together as best we can, as deep as we can.

Deep adaptation is part of what is needed now. It follows from the relentless logic that I have sought to pursue in these pages that we cannot avoid any longer actually preparing for a pretty full failure. And that doing so, paradoxically, is part of how we might yet wrench a greater success from the jaws of that failure. *But*, for many, deep adaptation is still too wrenching an ask. And it lacks a certain affirmative spirit (concerning what we can still be aiming for as a best-case scenario). And it doesn't put up front a certain sense of epistemic humility. For one thing we know for sure about the future we face: it is not possible to predict how it will play out, among the potential scenarios. (It is not possible because of our epistemic limitations. And it is not possible because it depends partly on what we chose to do.)

That is why for several years now I have been centering an agenda of transformative adaptation. First comprehensively outlined in the Green House collective work, *Facing up to climate reality*, that saw the light of day in 2019, *transformative* adaptation unlike 'deep adaptation' *aims* explicitly at a 'butterfly' scenario: it aspires to a change of system (like the transformation from endlessly-eating caterpillar to lighter-living butterfly) that will not require us to endure collapse before attaining a new civilisational footing.

Deep adaptation is necessary, but primarily *as an insurance policy*. Not as the main item of business. We have to level with people about how bad things are – that's how we get rocket-fuelled. By truth and authenticity. That was the secret of Greta's and XR's successes. But we have to avoid doomerist and fatalist urges, which are calamitous. We have to avoid such rash excessive knowingness, as if we *know* what the future holds. As I've made clear in the body of this book (see especially Chapter 9), it is a massive misreading of my work to find in it doomerism, an alleged inevitability that the future is f*cked and there is nothing we can do. On the contrary, the question is always: for what *can we now* continue actively to hope.

The golden mean, combining truth and agency, and avoiding Pollyannaism and doomism, is: aiming at transformation. *Mass* action is the only way we can realistically get that. I believe transformative adaptation has more potential mass appeal, for the foreseeable future, than deep adaptation. After elaborating on transformative adaptation in the following paragraphs, I'll turn to talking about the more general trend (of which it is an aspect), the trend that I term 'the (emerging, mass) moderate flank', that has more mass appeal, for the foreseeable future, than the radical flank that swept to (partial) success in 2019.

Transformative Adaptation is both honest about our predicament and can inspire people positively, while deep adaptation is bound (at least for the foreseeable future) to feel (to most) too overwhelmingly scary or sad. Moreover, and crucially, Transformative Adaptation practices epistemic humility, while deep adaptation (at least, in Jem Bendell's presentation of it) runs the risk of being too knowing; of sounding as if one *knows* what the future will be like (i.e., that it will be extreme in the extreme! That collapse is allegedly inescapable).

The struggle to define adaptation-in-action will, in my view, be nothing less than *the defining struggle of the rest of this decade.* (That is why I am working with Morgan Phillips and the Transformative Adaptation Collective on a book about transformative adaptation.[84])

The failure to get serious yet about transformative adaptation is above all a failure of *imagination.* 'Mitigation' (plus limited, defensive, shallow adaptation) is easier for our system to contemplate, because if you don't get serious about adaptation, then you don't have to imagine real change in the world. You can pretend that we can simply change what powers our energy/industrial system and enjoy a serene transition. If this was ever possible, then the book you are reading has laid out how it certainly isn't now.

Transformative adaptation is thus threatening to the status quo: it will shake things up, by threatening the shaky but still present consensus that the future will be some reduxed or reformed version of the present. And transformative adaptation demands attention to the priorities of those on the climate frontlines, especially in the Global South (where transformative adaptation has thus far *happened* on the ground more than in the Global North: because the crisis is felt much more directly and frequently in the Global South).

Adaptation has to date been the poor relation partly because the Global North has been more willing to fund mitigation than adaptation in the Global South. To date, mitigational action and talk has flourished far more than adaptational in part precisely because the direct benefits of mitigation in the Global South *for the Global North* are more than those of adaptation (in the Global South). What a scandal: we get the poor to mitigate, to help our global atmospheric commons, but we don't help them to adapt to the damage to that commons *that has been overwhelmingly caused by us in the Global North.*

Transformative adaptation is a both-and approach: mitigation *and* adaptation simultaneously and equally; being serious about climate justice *at the same time as* being serious about survival; a role for deep adaptation but *without* assuming we are already condemned to societal collapse; facing up to climate and ecology deterioration and decline without pretence or denial *and* believing in a positive vision for a better life, for a flourishing future; modelling a different future *and* continuing to carve out the space for that future through NVDA if and where necessary.

I believe that transformative adaptation is nothing less than an essential feature of any sane and efficacious response to our collective situation.

Transformative adaptation is one (crucial) example out of many of the emerging vein of thinking and organising that, since 2021, after moving on from being part of XR, I have provisionally termed 'the moderate flank'. Transformative adaptation functions as a moderate flank to both deep adaptation and XR. But the emerging moderate flank at large is actually and potentially a much wider movement.

'Moderate' is here defined with reference to – that is, relative to – extant radical flanks. Deep adaptation was created as a kind of radical flank to extant discourses of adaptation. Extinction Rebellion was formed quite explicitly as a radical flank to the existing 'environmental' movement; that is why XR chose as one of its very first actions the counter-intuitive target of Greenpeace HQ. The notion of radical flanks is well understood in social movement theory. The notion of forming a new mass moderate flank to a somewhat successful radical flank is my own innovation.

The fundamental insight of those of us who are seeking to help midwife a new mass moderate flank is that *what is needed is a far larger phalanx of people to march through the opened-wide Overton window that the radical flank created.* As I see it, the moderate flank will offer much larger numbers than have thus far been mobilised, and a way(s) of taking action that will not be off-putting. A manner of acting that will feel truly meaningful, and that will be grounded in a story – the story that it has been left too late for us to be able any longer to just outsource dealing with climate to others – that will emotionally mobilise in ways that the radical flank have started to show is possible, but cannot complete.

It might seem counter-intuitive to be 'moderate' when one absorbs the full truth. But remember, first, that this is only about being 'moderate' in terms of methods, *relative* to XR. It's not at all about moderating *what* we aim at achieving, let alone about reducing our truth-telling; on the very contrary. It's about creating an encompassing, welcoming climate movement, that mainstreams the appeal of what we are doing and aiming at.[85] For (by contrast) XR could not in the end break out of the bounds of the polarisation that it contributed to fostering. And this is hardly surprising; if you set out to win by way of polarising, as XR did, then you can hardly claim to be surprised when you polarise.

Climate *activism* (primarily through the 'radical flank') has had significant impacts in shifting public consciousness in recent years. But it has not mobilised *enough* participation to *effect* necessary change. And it has arguably hit a ceiling, numbers-wise. (That is likely to change – the volume of the radical flank is likely to rise again at some point in the 2020s, as, tragically, climatic conditions worsen; but for the next few years it is quite possible that the emerging moderate flank will have a monopoly on truly large numbers, among effective movements.) An increasingly large segment of the population is concerned about dangerous man-made climate change but not yet motivated to take significant action. One reason is that most concerned citizens do not want to become 'activists', do not want to take on that identity, and almost certainly will not. But they are hungry to take action, to know what to do. The climate movement's next wave will probably consist in large-scale, distributed climate and eco action, not just activism. In my view, this is exemplified by organising that is emerging in the form of such encouraging post-XR moderate flank endeavours as the Zero Hour campaign to get a climate and ecological emergency bill through Parliament, the emerging 'Climate Emergency Centres' network, community climate & eco action as found increasingly from the ground up, new inspiring organisations in the professions such as Lawyers For Net Zero, the heroic effort by some in the airline industry to transition and reduce their industry (the previously mentioned 'Safe Landing'); not to mention GreensCAN[86] and of course transformative adaptation. It is also exemplified by more below-the-radar action by insurers, fiduciaries, and many others to catalyse the kind of change needed in influential sectors of society.

Beyond the limited impact available to ordinary people in a neoliberalised world as voters and consumers alone, 'moderate flank' activity will likely coalesce, as the examples just cited attest, within core arenas of (individual and) *collective* agency; particularly workplaces (including here businesses and professions, as well as trades unions), and geographic communities. As well as tremendous latent power, these foci represent pressure points where climate vulnerability will increasingly present its own case for action.

A *mass* movement must be deliberately inclusive, e.g., of diverse political/identity groups and those unwilling or unable to risk their liberty through civil disobedience. This is another part of the picture of why what is now called for is a (mass) *moderate* flank. The inclusiveness I have in mind here is not the divisive pseudo-inclusiveness of most actually-existing, egocentric, anthropocentric 'equalities'-based ipolitics (aka 'intersectionalist' identity politics).[87] It is an inclusiveness that, rather, is serious about including the mainstream, including small-c conservatives, the working class and the underclass rather than only 'cosmopolitans' and the 'well-educated', and including those who have felt culturally or practically excluded from the radical flank. Activists, social justice warriors, the 'right-on', advocates of identity politics etc. should be participants and leaders in the moderate flank that we are building, provided of course that all are willing to accept and embrace the intention to reach far beyond the activist ghetto, and to be serious about engaging positively the mainstream. So as to be perceived to be and to *be* pragmatic, effective, *and* reality based. Rather than dogmatically or ideologically Leftist or 'woke-ist'.

The genuinely collective and constructive nature of the 'moderate flank' action will be crucial in mitigating the widespread fragmentation, hopelessness, and powerlessness (not to mention polarisation) that currently dampen response among climate concerned publics. Where individuals perceive themselves as too small to count, a perception of collective empowerment is a crucial motivator – not only to demand but to enact change, with positive social feedbacks then leading toward more such change.

Action at this level will function in the first instance directly, to reduce emissions and adapt to climate impacts. As for instance in determined local and localising resilience-building efforts: Transition Towns on speed, if you will. In many cases it will also and increasingly place pressure upon governments and large or powerful organisations to make changes at deeper leverage points. *However*, mobilisation at scale will *only* be possible if 'the story' changes. Endemic procrastination and 'outsourcing' of climate response to higher powers is validated by the pervasive 'five minutes to midnight' narrative that I've criticised in this book, that keeps people trusting that solutions are imminent, whether through government, tech, or indeed the existing climate movement.

The honest narrative shift offered in recent chapters, the shift to five past midnight, uproots this assumption, supporting widespread realisation that this sense of safety is founded on a lie. Climate impacts are upon us; a serene, tech-centric transition is no longer feasible.[88] Adaptation is unavoidable, and those we have trusted to keep us safe have not been honest (and have not kept us safe!).

In our experience thus far, stakeholders demonstrate responsiveness to this level of honesty; when the truth is genuinely accepted and understood, appropriate change is a logical response from the perspective of, for example, businesses in the interest of self-preservation as well as ethics. In other words, when radical honesty gets practised, then moderate-flank-style action and commitment emerge right out of it, naturally. When people with any openness in their mind and care in their hearts hear the truth about the ecological and climate more-than-emergency, provided it is delivered in a way that is both sensitive and direct, it is obvious to them that they need to become part of the emerging moderate flank, or something like it.

And the good news they then find? It's 'only' *five* past midnight… Things could be much worse. And of course they will be, unless, now that the time on the clock has been honestly acknowledged, we really set to work, and step into our full power. That's the aspiration that *is* the emerging, distributed moderate flank.

The moderate flank will be conducted via such 'truth-bombs' exploding in our minds (and hearts), truth-bombs along the lines essayed in this book.

It will be conducted via the power of the powerless outlined in key chapters of this book, by us taking matters reasonably and responsibly into our own hands, in ways that cannot be denied.

But it will also be based in our power insofar as we are materially powerful and influential: such as the power in the hands of lawyers or insurers, or in the hands of businesses. And perhaps in the hands of workers in energy-hungry sectors such as transport.

'Five past midnight' combines the power of the 'powerless' with real, insufficiently tapped elements of ordinary power into a potent cocktail. The new moderate flank is the unleashing of the hopes and dreams of ordinary millions.[89]

Genuine inclusivity is key to a potentially successful moderate flank.

The crisis is for everyone. To paraphrase Trotsky: you may not be interested in global over-heat, but global over-heat is interested in you. The moderate flank as I've envisaged it will be uncompromising on our situation, on the historic failure to respond appropriately green-wise to COVID-19 and Ukraine; while being positive on what we can actually do about it. Including, directly, ourselves, without having to ask others to do stuff for us. So, embracing democratic action (pretty much everyone can take action where they work, where they live), but solidly grounded in the truth (which, as we've seen, isn't pretty). The truth serves as a *grounding* and as the basis for the collective inner work which will be essential as we embark upon the long painful path of coming to terms with where we are.

The moderate flank, the next wave of the climate movement, extends telling the truth to be fully about 'ourselves'. XR has not succeeded *in getting its demands met in substance and will not* – 2025 is now just around the corner. A key success of XR, however, has been to open a space for others to have a chance to succeed. Aka, perhaps, 'the moderate flank'. (Liam Kavanagh and I are editing a book on this emerging distributed mass moderate flank. It will be replete with voices from within and around it.)[90]

It might still seem 'obvious' to some readers that radical truth-telling as expounded in this book most naturally fits with radical(-flank-style) action. But actually that's not necessarily true. Why? The radical flank gets constantly tempted away from levelling with us about the true desperate state of things because it is structurally tempted to fantasise that everything can be changed overnight, and so we can still be 'saved', and thus saved from having to face up to the age of consequences we are in. It is *easier* ultimately for the emerging 'moderate flank' to take up the mantle of truth-telling fully, including the embrace of transformative adaptation. This is because the new moderate flank understands that the journey to a possible societal sanity is not an overnight revolution, but rather a long and often hard slog (with painful losses and disasters inevitable along the way). So, accepting reality about there being no plausible pathway now to staying below 1.5°C of global over-heat, for instance, is – perhaps counter-intuitively but in fact – easier for moderate flankers than for radical flankers.

Let me be very clear and direct about this point, for it is both very important and slightly counter-intuitive. You want a successful 'mainstream'/'moderate' climate movement? Then don't shy away from the kind of truthfulness found in this book. For it's only in the outer reaches of the fantasy-land of feveredly over-optimistic radicals that we get to have a worldwide eco-socialist degrowth revolution or some such in the next couple of years that then turns everything around on the head of a pin. By contrast, being serious about a mass (and therefore pretty much by definition 'moderate') climate movement requires recognising the truth: that plainly everything is not going to transform overnight. And *that* in turn *requires* us to be realistic about the passing of some desperate and tragic climate milestones and probably some major tipping points in the coming decade or three, about the necessity of a massive attempt at 'adaptation', and so forth. (And that realisation *itself* can actually help us mobilise!)

What about a cheery 'stubborn optimism'? A mainstream approach that thinks that everything will come up roses? The point here is that even if this were somehow to happen – and my argument in recent chapters has been that there is no way that it will, for we only get to mass-mobilise on the basis of stirring a sense of betrayal, of shock, and thus of mourning, etc. – it is a lie to claim that it could feasibly happen with the speed that will keep us safe. A mass moderate movement that will magically sort everything worldwide in the next couple of years? That just isn't how moderate-style change works!

2025 for global net zero is impossible, while 2050 or even 2045 is too late; but *those* are the only dates that are feasible without a rapid (entirely implausible) worldwide triumph of degrowth or the like. The stubborn optimism programme (which has tended to be the basis on which the *old* moderate flank has operated) can only be supposed to save us at speed on the basis of deliberate manipulation and (at best) serious self-deception and self-delusion. Now is rather the time for stubborn realism, which requires the journey into the emotional pain of a world in decline, of an ocean of grief, and more.

And *that* makes possible the emotional *mobilisation*, the mourning and the consequent *organising*, that has been the trajectory of this book.

I believe that the power of authentic emotional responsiveness to our unprecedented plight, the power that has been demonstrated by Greta and XR, has only just begun to be tapped. The new moderate flank will include a deeper tapping of the mighty power that is a parent's love, cross-cutting everything else, and more generally will tap into the power of the 'five past midnight' narrative. We, and *a fortiori* our children, have been badly let down. And we are not going to be complicit in that failure any longer. We will not allow our trust to be abused further, and we do not want our psyches to be handled with kid-gloves. We want to be treated like adults. We are ready to face climate-reality, to face up to what it is too late for, and then to strive with determination for what it is not too late for.

In sum: We have been rendered highly vulnerable, and, as that is processed, the 'moderate flank' will grow, and can achieve the kinds of consciousness shifts and practice changes intimated above.

That could conceivably be enough to prevent climate collapse, and climate- and eco-driven societal collapse, even now. For we could get into a virtuous circle, at last, here: as people see more and more of their peers moving to act, in their own 'area' and more broadly across society, more and more could come on board, realising that (at the last) we may have something that is at sufficient scale to make the needful difference.

Accordingly, the emerging moderate flank will be the central locale of my own endeavours in the coming years. I hope it might be of yours, too. Whoever you are, reader. For the beauty of the mass moderate flank proposal is that it is for everyone. Pretty much everyone works somewhere, and everyone lives somewhere. The invitation to join the moderate flank is an invitation to act where *you* have potential power.

Hope of the hopeless? A remark on the place of higher education and philosophy in relation to truth

In this book, I've spoken quite a lot about 'the power of the powerless'. There's another, historic name for it: satyagraha. Gandhi's great concept and form, which can be translated as 'truth-force'.

It's symbolically present in the thought-rupturing image on the cover of this book. What we need is to see, to *feel*, and then to manifest, the *shock* of how our system's gross mistreatment of the Earth is akin to a *tear in reality itself*. We are not truly awake until that shock has an effect on us akin to that which the woodcutter inside Agim Sulaj's extraordinary image is beginning to experience. Until, that is to say, we have broken out of the hall of mirrors of 'post-modernism', the nonsense of 'post-truth', to feel the terrible truth as deeply as that. This whole slow civilisational suicide that we have as yet been unable to arrest is not a bad dream; it's really happening. The frame through which we render things somehow manageable itself needs to be broken, and then perhaps we will see fact to face. Tears are part of this process; the process of coming to terms with the scale of the loss that is upon us. The process of eco-grief, eco-terror – and eco-anger.

While I spend part of my time now working for the Moderate Flank Incubator that we've created to help grow the young moderate next wave of climate action, I remain a half-time academic. This book has centred upon a very-much-more-than-academic vision. Before I end, though, I want to make a remark about why academics matter hereabouts: how voices of the likes of my university colleagues can make a distinctive difference. What our particular *role* is in relation to action on the crisis; action, that is, that fits the scale of the mind-bending tragedy that our civilisation has unleashed.

The point is a very simple one. Of course, I've argued in this book that everyone ought to be levelling with themselves and with each other. But the roles of certain groups are especially stark and weighty. The media, for instance, obviously. In the case of academics, *our* role focally is about telling the whole truth, including in our classes, to our students; including in our 'impact' work, to policy-makers, etc., and *including the crucial truth that a factual discourse alone has failed.*[91] The whole truth includes that failure, and one's emotional response to it, and of course to the crisis and our collective failure in respect of it. To our desperate condition.

What are academics *for*, if not to inquire fearlessly into the whole truth? To *abide* there, whether that leads to comfortable outcomes *or not*.

Thus academics are now called upon to own up – as academics and as human beings and as citizens – to the failure of the information-deficit model, the idea that all we needed was to supply facts (information) and then they would be acted on. For, as set out in Chapter 11, such a *congruent* move beyond our narrow professional role is a part of what it means to exist adequately in a situation of more-than-emergency.

We are called, that is, to confess our own 'powerlessness'; to full disclosure, including, in our case, of the categorical failures of the 'information deficit' model[92] of action on climate *and* of the (linked) 'rational decision-maker' model of policy-change. (By way of confessing our own inefficacy comes an incalculable power. As I argued in chapters 5, 6, and 10.)

Some readers might be surprised that, while that *theme* has featured heavily in this book, I haven't spoken much about the *complexities* of truth itself. As a philosopher I'm of course well aware of these. But one theme of my book (and of this Conclusion) has been that there is also a *simplicity* to truth that has sometimes been lost sight of in academia and in academically influenced versions of activism over the last couple of generations. For instance, in relation to climate denial: full-scale post-truthism is deadly. And certain academic trends such as post-modernism have been accommodating of and supportive of absurd deadly ideas, such as post-truth. One hopes that the rise of Trump has put an end to liberal indulgence of post-modernism and brought back the sense amongst everyone – perhaps other than the far Right – that there really is truth and falsehood, not endlessly multiple truths.

Such a realisation is integral to the success of the suggestions and ideas that this book has consisted in and insisted on– and on, I believe, mobilising.

In terms of where my approach stands in relation to the history of philosophy, it can be simply placed. I stand opposed to the influential tradition, introduced by Plato, of the 'noble lie'. My reasoning is simple. There's a problem with lies, however 'noble'. The clue is in their name. They're lies. (Unless they are self-consciously, openly presented as fictions or myths, in which case the harm of their sting is withdrawn.) An influential recent example of a 'noble' lie is the 3.5% theory that was presented as 'scientific' truth by XR.[93] As I've shown previously, Erica Chenoweth's claim that all we need is to get 3.5% of people protesting on the streets to suddenly magically win our full demands for change is pseudo-scientific hopium.

Moreover, such claims are *manipulative,* as is the ongoing 1.5°C delusion as promulgated by NGOs, 'leaders' and scientists who in truth know better. Such claims are attempts to squeeze action out of a public who instead ought to be treated – and trusted – as equals.

At this time, more than ever, we need truth-tellers. Whistle-blowers. But this begins at home. Nothing is more important now than for academics, and especially scientists, to sound the alarm in a straightforward, honest, and precautionary manner. For others *rely* upon this honesty, on our expertise.

I want *you* to demand that scientists (and everyone else) level with you. Insist that you have had enough of bromides. That the IPCC's too-slow journey toward the truth, for all the good intentions of those within the

IPCC, doesn't satisfy you. And that it's time for us together to grow up. Maturity means a willingness to hear, face, *and act on* difficult truths.

The truth of our vulnerability and the surrounding truths that have been the topic and hallmark of this book need trumpeting much more clearly. In ways that are *congruent*: action meeting words. Academics et al. need to come clean about their fears, about their 'powerlessness', about the future.

And at the end of the day, as I said at the very start of this book, this really ought to go without saying. If someone is unhealthily over-weight, does one help them by pretending they are not? If someone has cancer, haven't we got over thinking that we ought to whisper the truth to their loved ones but not to them? If someone is addicted to opiates, are you really going to pretend otherwise? Especially if you love them, you will tell them the truth. Lovingly, carefully, in the right setting, but in the end without reservation.

We are addicted to fossil fuels. Some of us are addicted to greed, to money, to *things*. Our system is addicted to growth. These addictions are killing us and (more importantly) everyone we love and care about, including the voiceless future ones and more-than-human beings.

End of story...

The beautiful coincidence

But let no one accuse me of spreading 'doom and gloom'. There's another truth that's well-hidden, this one about well-being. It's what I call the beautiful coincidence. It's a *convenient* truth. The point is that by and large the very things we need to do in order to prevent or at least soften eco-driven collapse are the very things we need to do in order to make our lives better. To create more flourishing, more community, more security. A more local future, with more democracy, more time, slower, more meaningful.[94]

And spiritually speaking, the desperate situation is at the same time… necessary, and even has a dimension of beauty. We are called to be what the Dao De Jing calls 'men and women of calling'.[95] What more (painful but) beautiful gift is there than being alive at a time of necessary, fateful, still-hope-imbued transformation? *This* civilisation is finished. Not civilisation as such! A better one can be what comes next. And while the process of getting there is now bound to be very hard, recall the good news that lies hidden in plain view in the epochal metaphor that I've marshalled in the second half of this book: it's 'only' five past midnight… How very good, to be here and now living in truth, which is existentially good in itself. We can still, moreover, make an unparalleled difference to the conditions that will govern our own existence and that of the multitude of beings to follow us.

The hard and yet empowering truth that *this* civilisation is finished, that the smooth transition to a sustainable society is in the rearview mirror, is the best basis for *realising* the beautiful coincidence.

The moral *of the story*

And finally, in case you are wondering: my sister went ahead and bought the rabbit anyway.[96] And the story ends happily. It has turned out to be the most delightful creature, not biting or whatever as un-handled rabbits sometimes do. The family treated it very well, from the start, to be fair. So perhaps it's not surprising. They treated it with extra care and love and attention, knowing about its past. The *moral* of the story? Obviously, that – like it or not – it really is best to know the truth.

A happy ending... I bet you didn't expect *that* when you picked up this book.[97]

Acknowledgements

First, huge thanks to Samuel Alexander, my long-time collaborator, who has overseen the production of this book and served as my editorial guide. But those phrases underplay what has been his real role. In many ways, he edited this book just as thoroughly and substantively (i.e., inducing all manner of changes and improvements) as he did my previous books with him on XR and on *this* civilisation being finished. Thanks mate!

Thanks also to Antoinette Wilson for proofreading, once again. Many thanks to Agim Sulaj for generously granting permission for me to use his startling image on the cover (artwork by Agim Sulaj © http://www.agimsulaj.com/). And thanks to Sharon France from Looking Glass Press for cover design and typesetting.

Thanks to the various outlets that have given permission for the pieces included here that were previously published to be reprinted: *Writers Rebel, Green World, Brave New Europe, Emerge,* and *Resilience.*

In terms of the content of the book, I am greatly indebted to Marc Lopatin and Wolfgang Knorr for their co-authorship of two key chapters in the book: Chapters 11 and 12. They are both superb interlocutors, true spirits of truth.

I am further indebted to Marc for his persistent thought-leadership on vulnerability, safety, truth-telling, and 1.5; much of my own thinking in this book takes off from or indeed in effect reformulates his. This book would not have been possible without his collaborative thought-leadership.

Thanks for ideas and inspiration to Adam Woodhall, Skeena Rather, Gail Bradbrook, Jem Bendell, Caroline Lucas, and my GreensCAN colleagues including especially Laura Baldwin and Alison Teal.

Thanks also to Michael Dowd, Deane Spillane-Walker, Ed Gemmell, Cynthia Riddell, Dale Walkonen, Clare Farrell, Jessica Townsend, Victor Anderson, George Marshall, Liam Kavanagh, Paddy Loughman, Phoebe Tickell, Rosie Bell, Scott Henery, Ed Gillespie, Adrian Ramsay, John Foster, Roger Hallam, Michael Gove, Tim O'Riordan, Juliette Harkin, Sam Earle, Roger Creagh-Osborne, Jon Alexander, Helena Norberg-Hodge, Oona Menges, Joe Eastoe, Atus Mariqueo-Russell, Chris Smaje, George Monbiot, Alastair McIntosh, and Jonathon Porritt.

Big thanks to Victor Anderson and Peter Kramer for thorough readings of the whole manuscript that have resulted in improvements on almost every page. Thanks to Joe Eastoe for invaluable research assistance in pulling together the bibliographical document that follows.

Thanks finally to my students who have listened to and welcomed my truth-telling these last seven years.

This book is dedicated to my amazing sister, Councillor Tess Read, without whom its framing would not have been possible!

Annotated bibliography of fundamental readings

Anderson, K., 'Even "climate progressive" nations fall far short of Paris Agreement targets', 16 June 2020.
Available via https://www.manchester.ac.uk/discover/news/even-climate-progressive-nations-fall-far-short-of-paris-agreement-targets/.
Sets out how the Paris Agreement is in effect a pipe dream.

Bendell, J. and R. Read, Deep Adaptation: Navigating the realities of climate chaos (Oxford: Policy, 2021).
Investigates deep adaptation (and to some extent transformative adaptation). Chapter 1 is particularly salient for providing a fundamental basis for Do you want to know the truth?, *in that it lays out 'What Climate Science Can and Cannot Tell Us About Our Predicament'.*

Eyring, V. et al., 'Status of the Coupled Model Intercomparison Project Phase 6 and Goals of the Workshop' (2019), Coupled Model Intercomparison Project. Available at: https://cmip6workshop19.sciencesconf.org/data/CMIP6_CMIP6AnalysisWorkshop_Barcelona_190325_FINAL.pdf
Shows that recent climate models are tending to predict effects worse than those of older models, resulting in some showing over 2 degrees of warming more than was previously predicted. This is thought to be due to the tipping points and cascade effects referenced elsewhere in this bibliography. This item also details how the IPCC reports may be guilty of downplaying the true severity of dangerous climate change.

Gentine, P. et al., 'Large influence of soil moisture on long-term terrestrial carbon uptake', Nature (2019), Vol. 565, pp 476–479.
Dryer-than-normal years (due to heatwaves or droughts) have seriously compromised the ability of soil to capture carbon. The land's role of being an efficient carbon sink is reaching its limit. As a result, more

human-emitted greenhouse gases will end up in the atmosphere instead of being absorbed in the ground, compounding warming effects and accelerating climate-dangerous effects.

Hausfather, Z., and R. Betts, 'Analysis: How "carbon-cycle feedbacks" could make global warming worse', *Carbon Brief* (2020). Available at: https://www.carbonbrief.org/analysis-how-carbon-cycle-feedbacks-could-make-global-warming-worse/
Details the effect of feedback loops which, through uncertainty over the climate models of scientists, mean that mainstream science may well be understating the climate threat. The reality of climate breakdown may be worse than the models predict due to this uncertainty, which could result in 25% more warming, and possibly incalculably more. For example, about half of emitted carbon remains in the atmosphere with the rest being absorbed by the sea or land. As these become saturated, they will be less capable of absorbing as much carbon, resulting in more persisting in the atmosphere, compounding already grave warming predictions.

Hood, M., 'Scientists warn multiple overlapping crises could trigger "global systematic collapse"', *Science Alert* (2020). Available at: https://www.sciencealert.com/hundreds-of-top-scientists-warn-combined-environmental-crises-will-cause-global-collapse
Two hundred scientists warn that the risks from climate damage are not being communicated effectively, and that the tendency of scientists and politicians to focus on one problem at a time makes it difficult to suitably confront the multi-faceted nature of climate risk. Instead, overlapping risks of food insecurity, extreme weather events, biodiversity decline, and freshwater pollution, as well as many more, are capable of combining and amplifying each other causing 'global systemic collapse'.

IPCC, IPCC Sixth Assessment Report 2022 (2022). Available at: https://www.ipcc.ch/report/ar6/wg2/
The most recent report from the United Nations International Panel on Climate Change, compiled by 234 scientists and built from over 14,000 research papers. Argues that limiting warming to 1.5 degrees, as was originally the aim of the Paris Agreement of 2015, is now extremely unlikely,

showing that 1.5 degrees of warming is likely to be a reality by 2040 at the latest. The report details how manmade climate change is already transforming every inhabited region in the world, causing rising climate instability through, amongst other things, more frequent severe weather events. It is considered the starkest warning of climate damage published by the IPCC, confirming its status as an existential threat. (As David Spratt and Ian Dunlop detailed in What Lies Beneath: The understatement of existential climate risk, the IPCC have systematically tended to downplay the true threat of dangerous anthropogenic climate change due to their methodological emphasis on consensus, their generally 'calming', distanced language, their reports taking years to complete, their summaries being doctored by governments, etc. The Sixth Report is the least vulnerable to this charge yet, but aspects of the charge remain true.)

Kemp, L. et al., 'Climate Endgame: Exploring catastrophic climate change scenarios' (2022), *PNAS* 119:34. Available at: https://www.pnas.org/doi/10.1073/pnas.2108146119
Investigates extreme climate scenarios and proposes a systematic agenda for their further investigation, of which to date there has been too little in the academic world.

Knorr, W. et al., 'After coronavirus, focus on the climate emergency', originally published in *The Guardian* (2020). Available at: https://www.theguardian.com/world/2020/may/10/after-coronavirus-focus-on-the-climate-emergency
Argues that the huge bailouts fossil fuel companies are receiving from governments around the world signify 'game over for preventing dangerous climate change' and will make the mitigation of temperature rise under 2 degrees impossible. Urges for honesty 'to acknowledge our collective failure to respond to climate change'. Stresses that post-pandemic economies should reorganise to adequately tackle the climate crisis. As of 2022, this hope has not become a reality.

Lamarche-Gagnon, G. et al., 'Greenland melt drives continuous export of methane from the ice-sheet bed', *Nature* (2019), Vol. 565, p.73–77.
Details the risk of declining ice sheets in Greenland. This research shows active methanogenic wetlands lie under these icesheets. Methane is c.25 times more 'proficient' than CO_2 at trapping heat in the atmosphere. Thus, permafrost decline will cause ripple effects to worsen and accelerate the effects of global climate damage.

Lenton, Timothy M., et al., 'Climate tipping points – too risky to bet against', *Nature* (2019). Available at: https://www.nature.com/articles/d41586-019-03595-0
Collects data showing that tipping points are both more likely and more catastrophic than previously thought. Notably, this piece shows that key tipping points may be activated between 1 and 2 degrees above preindustrial levels (as of the time of writing the planet's surface temperate was already well above 1 degree above this level). Moreover, this article warns of potential global 'tipping cascades', where the devastation in one key ecosystem (e.g., Amazon rainforest, Greenland's ice sheet, coral reefs, etc.) could cause other ecosystems to collapse in a domino effect. Tipping points also make our calculated carbon budgets woefully inaccurate in preventing widespread ecological calamity.

Moses, A. '"Collapse of Civilisation is the Most Likely Outcome": Top Climate Scientists'. Available at: https://www.resilience.org/stories/2020-06-08/collapse-of-civilisation-is-the-most-likely-outcome-top-climate-scientists/
Asher Moses sets out evidence that the collapse of society might now be inevitable due to 9 of the known 15 'tipping points' crossing sustainable limits. The important point about this piece is that it draws upon detailed remarks about closely related matters by a number of top experts in the field, including Will Steffen, Australia's top climate scientist; Hans Schellnhuber, the leading climate-policy expert in Germany; and Johan Rockström, leader of the 'Planetary Boundaries' approach to the Earth system. The piece brings together systems thinkers with climate scientists, to provide a more comprehensive interdisciplinary overview of existential

climate risk than is usual. A key point from the piece to note is that the transition to a zero-carbon economy may easily take over 30 years, whilst it might already be too late to prevent environmental damage from causing the collapse of society as we know it. (This piece inaccurately represents Rockström's views on one detail; his actual view as accurately quoted in The Guardian piece linked to here turns out to be not a great deal more reassuring: https://www.theguardian.com/environment/2019/ may/18/climate-crisis-heat-is-on-global-heating-four-degrees-2100- change-way-we-live.)

Potsdam Institute for Climate Impacts Research, 'Planetary boundaries update', *PICIR* (2022). Available at: https://www.pik-potsdam.de/en/ news/latest-news/planetary-boundaries-update-freshwater-bound- ary-exceeds-safe-limits .
Helpful authoritative explainer on the widely respected 'planetary bound- aries' framework. The primary focus of this book has been the climate, because of its centrality to public debate and because of the scale of the existential threat it poses to humankind. However, there are nine planetary boundaries of which climate is only one. This piece shows how we have now transgressed six of those nine boundaries and are thus well outside any 'safe operating space'. Moreover, vis-a-vis three of those boundaries, including biodiversity/biospherical integrity, studies suggest that they are in a worse state of unsafety and of novelty even than our climate.

Read, R., 'The Precautionary Principle and climate change', com- missioned by the UK All Party Parliamentary Group on Agroecology, 2018. Available at: https://agroecology-appg.org/ourwork/ap- pg-briefings-on-the-precautionary-principle-climate-change-and-ani- mal-welfare/
Explains how the Precautionary Principle requires us to stay ahead of consensus climate science in order for us to stay in any kind of safe zone.

Read, R., Why Climate Breakdown Matters. (London: Bloomsbury Academic, 2022).
My most recent book about climate and ecology looks at the philosophi- cal case for caring about future people and the philosophical implications

of impending climate breakdown. It contains discussions of ecological grief, climate disasters, and community. It is written in the first instance for an academic audience, but also so as to be popularly accessible.

Ripple, W. et al., 'World Scientists' Warning of Climate Emergency', *BioScience* (2020), Vol.70, Issue 1, pp8–12.
A declaration signed by more than 11,000 scientists warning of the severity of the climate crisis. Amongst other things, the piece laments high-income consumption, meat production, and fossil fuel usage being driving forces of environmental degradation. Moreover, the article warns of rising sea levels, disappearing arctic ice, and the collapse of biodiversity around the world, concluding that climate decline is accelerating quicker than was first imagined. A key take-away is the emphasis given to tipping points and reinforcing feedback loops, which the scientists highlight as a key concern.

Sagan, C., 'Carl Sagan testifying before Congress in 1985 on Climate Change' (1985). Available to watch at: https://www.youtube.com/watch?v=Wp-WiNXH6hI
Climate scientist and public figure Carl Sagan highlights to Congress the risk of the greenhouse effect resulting from the combustion of fossil fuels. Sagan warns of 'several-centigrade-degree temperature increase' which could be a reality midway through the next century. He urges immediate action to reduce the burning of fossil fuels and 'do the right thing' for 'our children and grandchildren'. This signifies one of the earliest major warnings on climate, and greatly influenced Al Gore, who was present. Now, 37 years later, Sagan's testimony is a sad reminder that climate science has been solid and pretty much irrefutable for decades and international action has been grossly inadequate.

Scholars Warning, 8 Feb. 2021, published simultaneously in *The Guardian* and *Le Monde*. Available at: http://iflas.blogspot.com/2021/02/over-500-sign-scholarswarning-on.html.
Over 500 academics warn of the risk of potential societal collapse due to climate collapse.

Steffen, W. et al., 'Trajectories of the Earth System in the Anthropocene', *PNAS* (2018). Available at: https://www.pnas.org/content/pnas/early/2018/07/31/1810141115.full.pdf
Focuses on the effect of climate tipping points causing ecological cascades. For example, the decline of Greenland's ice sheets due to global temperature rise will release a huge amount of trapped greenhouse gases, further exacerbating climate change beyond current predictions. Our current trajectory may result in what the authors call a Hothouse Earth, a situation where global agriculture output is devastated, and adaptation is effectively impossible. Whilst this article urges immediate and widespread action to reduce emissions and protect ecosystems, it also warns that even these actions may not be sufficient.

World Meteorological Organisation, 'WMO Statement on the State of the Global Climate in 2018', *WMO* (2019). Available at https://library.wmo.int/doc_num.php?explnum_id=5789
Explores multiple aspects of the climate crisis, warning of extreme risk to global food supply and showing that mass displacement from climate chaos is already occurring and is expected to only get worse. This study details that the rise in sea levels is increasing at an unprecedented level, with average sea levels increasing by around 3.15mm every year between 1993 and 2017, and that this rate is likely to increase.

Xu, Y., V. Ramanathan, and D. Victor, 'Global warming will happen faster than we think', *Nature* (2019), Vol.564, pp30–32. Available at: https://www.nature.com/articles/d41586-018-07586-5
The authors warn that warming may be far worse than the IPCC predicts, since emissions are still rising, 'global dimming' has been increasing (but will diminish in coming decades, with potential quasi-'termination-shock' effects), and the planet may be entering a natural warm phase (not caused by humans, but it will amplify the damage of anthropocentric climate change). These effects reinforce each other, and the researchers conclude that 'safe' limit of 1.5°C of over-heating will be (b)reached by 2030, with 2 degrees being reached by 2050.

Endnotes

1 There is of course a wrinkle here. Asking the question is, in itself, a revelation which tacitly foregrounds the fact that the truth could be hidden, which is very different from simply hiding the truth. Even a child would probably understand that if the rabbit had been handled much *there would be no need for the man to ask her whether she wanted to know the truth*, because he would just tell her the good news. So, by asking the question the man did already in effect indirectly tell her the truth about the lack of handling. If my sister had answered, 'No, I don't want to know the truth', she could only be trying to avoid facing a truth she already more or less knew. But ... why would the man not just tell her the truth directly, instead of communicating it vaguely and indirectly? And, more broadly, are there analogues between the state of would-be disavowal of the truth – knowing it secretly while trying to avoid it or to 'softly' deny it – that presumably the rabbit-seller unconsciously projected onto my sister, on the one hand, and the state that many of us find ourselves in individually or collectively with regard to (facing or not facing) climate-truth, on the other? As this book proceeds, I shall increasingly suggest that the answer to the latter question is: Yes, there are. And that this is of great importance and is a state of affairs that cannot – must not – be sustained.

2 I treat of some of those newest movements explicitly in the Conclusion to this book.

3 Why scare-quote 'emergency'? The reason why will become clear in Chapter 11...

4 See Thomas Berry, 1999, *The Great Work: Our Way into the Future*. New York: Harmony/Bell Tower.

5 Not that my previous writing had been exactly untruthful; but what I was thinking and writing now seemed by contrast with it to have succeeded in peeling away unconscious moments of evasion in where I'd been before.

6 See Rupert Read, 2022, *Why Climate Breakdown Matters*, London: Bloomsbury.

7 Rupert Read, 2017. 'This Civilisation is Finished', *GreenTalk* (8 June 2017). Available here: https://greentalk.org.uk/this-civilisation-is-finished/ (accessed 2 September 2022).

8 Rupert Read, 2018. 'Shed a Light: Rupert Read – This Civilisation is Finished: So What is to be Done?' Public lecture, delivered at Churchill College, University of Cambridge, 7 November 2018. Available here: https://www.youtube.com/watch?v=uzCxFPzdO0Y (accessed 2 September 2022).

9 Rupert Read and Samuel Alexander, 2020, *Extinction Rebellion: Insights from the Inside*. Melbourne: Simplicity Institute.

10 Rupert Read and Ronan Harrington, 2020. 'Where Does Extinction Rebellion Go from Here?' Online Conversation, 5 August 2020. Available here: https://www.youtube.com/watch?v=1KqZAsi3w4c (accessed 2 September 2022).

11 A full glare of publicity finally beamed onto this address with the accession in 2022 to the UK premiership of Liz Truss, a darling of the libertarian think tanks based in Tufton Street: see e.g. "The other black door", available at: https://www.bbc.co.uk/sounds/play/m001c65m.

12 Marc Lopatin, Skeena Rathor, and Rupert Read. Undated. 'Rushing the "Emergency"'. Online publication. Available here: https://xrstroud.org/wp-content/uploads/2020/01/XR-Story-Vision2020-Leaflet.V11.pdf (accessed 2 September 2022).

13 This might seem a surprising claim. Hasn't XR's former spokesperson Roger Hallam, for instance, been criticised not unreasonably for being at times too alarmist, too catastrophic in his predictions of the future? Yes; but *at the same time* Roger has typically held out hope that all this could be turned around, and we could be kept below 1.5 degrees successfully, with sufficient action prior to 2025. This is hopium and leads to desperation and burnout. (See chapters 11 and 12 of this book for some detailing of this point.) The radical flank (unlike the moderate flank) is subject to a structural temptation to stay in fantasy land, imagining itself leading us swiftly – messianically – to salvation.

14 If the complexity of these paragraphs is daunting, I can only urge you, reader, to await chapters 5 and 6 – or, if you prefer, to skip ahead to them now.

15 As mentioned above, my talk 'This civilisation is finished' at Cambridge began with this admission of common (and personal) failure.

16 The underlying reason for the resistance to truth here is of course this: People resist absorbing the truth on climate and ecology because it's the thin end of a larger wedge... The large wedge being the truth about the un-sustainable civilisation we have. Much will have to be given up, in the decades to come.

17 Correspondence from my former colleague, renowned truth-telling climate scientist Prof. Kevin Anderson, 22 June 2022: "To offer a 99% chance of not exceeding 1.5°C, I suggest we would have to eliminate CO_2 now, i.e. no [carbon] budget. The temperature would still rise as a new equilibrium established itself, with aerosols etc reducing and some small inertia in terms of oceans (possible outgassing) and other GHG feedbacks that are in train. So, if we want the nearest we can now get to a guarantee of not exceeding 1.5°C – then I'd suggest an immediate cessation of CO_2 – but even this would leave some risk of 1.5°C." Confidence beyond reasonable doubt, rather than supposed 50% or 67% chances of staying below it, is a very reasonable ask. 50% or 67% are very bad bets: would you get on a plane that had a 67% chance of arriving?

18 See n.17, immediately above, for a compelling source on this. Kevin has now gone even further: in conversation with me at the Speakers Forum of the Green Gathering in August 2022, he said, 'I wouldn't put a penny on us staying below 1.5 degrees, *even if you gave me incredible odds*'. This is in effect coming clean that there simply is no even-remotely-plausible pathway to staying below 1.5 degrees. See on this also the massive recent intervention from Scientist Rebellion, here: https://twitter.com/scientistrebel1/

status/1580136245413322754 . Several hundred scientists and academics have now made the same declaration.

19 Bronwyn Adcock, 2022. 'The Hope and Climate Catastrophe Roadshow: "There's Just This Thirst for Optimistic Story", *The Guardian* (3 April 2022). Available here: https://www.theguardian.com/film/2022/apr/03/the-hope-and-climate-catastrophe-roadshow-theres-just-this-thirst-for-optimistic-story (accessed 2 September 2022).

20 Again, it wouldn't necessarily have been wrong at an earlier stage – e.g., when UNFCCC was signed in 1992. *The problem is sticking to what we've always said when the real situation has drastically moved on.*

21 Lauren Berlant, 2011. *Cruel Optimism.* Durham: Duke University Press.

22 This book doesn't delve much into these (obviously essential) facets of the climate conundrum, except in the short Tufton Street related chapters. For detailed discussion of the vested interests/raw power dimensions of our predicament, particularly strong sources include Jason Hickel's work, Dario Kenner's work, and the recent BBC series 'Big oil vs the world'.

23 *Some* of that case is present here, however, especially at points in the longer essays in the second half (and in the references to authoritative sources that I have included at various key points). But the case can be found much more fully elsewhere in my oeuvre (especially in the book that Jem Bendell and I published, *Deep Adaptation*, and in the first half of my recent book *Why Climate Breakdown Matters*). As I say, further evidential support is represented within the present work by the 'Fundamental Bibliography'. This succinct annotated bibliography contains key sources which you can consult, if you need them, to back up fully a fundamental attitude expounded *and taken up* in this work: one of confidence that the truth on climate and ecology is, tragically, on balance, significantly worse than most people realise – or have dared to say. Moreover, if you are reading the eBook version of this book, many more sources are instantly available at your fingertips: via the additional hyperlinks included in the eBook.

24 Rupert Read, 2017. 'Why I had to tell my students that I fear for them', *Medium* (28 January 2017). Available here: https://medium.com/@ GreenRupertRead/why-i-had-to-tell-my-students-that-i-fear-for-them-64bf1625b878 (accessed 7 September 2022). The attentive reader will already have noticed that several of the shorter texts gathered in this book were originally given as speeches. This has meant that at times there are elements of repetition in what you'll find here. Please forgive those — or, naturally, feel so free to skip any bits of the book that feel unduly repetitious to you.

25 Nassim Nicholas Taleb, Rupert Read, Raphael Douady, et al. 2014. 'The Precautionary Principle (with application to the Genetic Modification of Organisms)'. Extreme Risk Initiative – NYU School of Engineering Working Paper Series (17 October 2014). Available here: https://arxiv.org/ pdf/1410.5787.pdf (accessed 7 September 2022).

26 See Damian Carrington, 2012. 'Future Generations Risk "Enslavement" without a Vote Now', *The Guardian* (5 January 2012). Available here: https://www.theguardian.com/environment/damian-carrington-blog/2012/jan/04/climate-politics-future-generation-justice (accessed 22 September 2022).

27 And there are, moreover, precedents for and partial extant enactments of such guardians: for detail, see early sections of my report *Guardians of the Future: A constitutional case for representing and protecting future people* (Green House, 2012).

28 Nigel Lawson, the former UK Chancellor, is the frontman for the Global Warming Policy Foundation that HQs in Tufton Street.

29 Rupert Read, 2021. 'Rupert Read's Court Statement', *Writers Rebel* (5 November 2021). Available here: https://writersrebel.com/rupert-reads-court-statement/ (accessed 7 September 2022).

30 Matthew Cantor, 2019. 'Could "Climate Delayer" become the political epithet of our times', *The Guardian* (1 March 2019). Available here: https://www.theguardian.com/environment/2019/mar/01/could-climate-delayer-become-the-political-epithet-of-our-times (accessed 7 September 2022).

31 See, e.g., https://www.opendemocracy.net/en/dark-money-investigations/think-tanks-adam-smith-policy-exchange-legatum-iea-taxpayers-alliance-climate-denial/

32 For a full definition of Transformative Adaptation visit https://transformative-adaptation.com/

33 Josh Gabatiss and Robert McSweeny, 2021. 'CCC: Adaptation to Climate Risks "Underfunded and Ignored" by UK Government', *CarbonBrief* (16 June 2021). Available here: https://www.carbonbrief.org/ccc-adaptation-to-climate-risks-underfunded-and-ignored-by-uk-government/ (accessed 7 September 2022).

34 See Chapters 7, 8, and 10 for what did in fact happen at COP26; much along the lines of my projection in this speech.

35 Rupert Read and Laura Baldwin, 2021. 'The Politics of Paradox', *Green World* (5 July 2021). Available here: https://greenworld.org.uk/article/politics-paradox (accessed 8 September 2022).

36 Vaclav Havel, 1978. 'The Power of the Powerless', *Non-violent Conflict* (1978). Available here: https://www.nonviolent-conflict.org/wp-content/uploads/1979/01/the-power-of-the-powerless.pdf (accessed 8 September 2022).

37 Ben Robinson, 2020. 'Even "Climate Progressive" Nations Fall Far Short of Paris Agreement Targets', Manchester (Online, 16 June 2020). Available here: https://www.manchester.ac.uk/discover/news/even-climate-progressive-nations-fall-far-short-of-paris-agreement-targets/ (accessed 8 September 2022).

38 Rupert Read, 'This Civilisation is Finished: What is to be Done?', IFLAS Occasional Paper 3 (10 December 2018). Available here: http://lifeworth.com/IFLAS_OP_3_rr_whatistobedone.pdf (accessed 8 September 2022).

39 Vijay Kolinjivadi, 2020. 'The Coronavirus Outbreak is Part of the Climate Crisis', *Al Jazeera* (30 March 2020). Available here: https://www.aljazeera.com/opinions/2020/3/30/the-coronavirus-outbreak-is-part-of-the-climate-change-crisis/ (accessed 8 September 2022).

40 Green Party, n.d. 'Philosophical Basis of the Green Party' *GreenPartyUK*. Available at: https://policy.greenparty.org.uk/philosophical-basis.html (accessed 8 September 2022).

41 Joseph Eastoe, 2021. '10 Tests for COP26: The Verdict', *Green World* (23 November 2021). Available at: https://greenworld.org.uk/article/10-tests-cop26-verdict (accessed 8 September 2022).

42 Die Grünen are now in shared power in Germany.

43 See the Conclusion to the present work for some detail on how we are going to do it.

44 An encouraging straw in the wind more recently is the very positive response I received from the elected Greens gathered at the Association of Green Councillors when I gave a talk on the GreensCAN strategy at their Conference: see https://www.youtube.com/watch?v=Z90Kl1f-w0g for the full talk and Q&A.

45 After COP26, I went on to propose in an article in the *Independent* that there should indeed be no more COPs: https://www.independent.co.uk/climate-change/climate-crisis-cop26-glasgow-b1969781.html .

46 I owe this point to Elizabeth May.

47 This happened: https://bravenewmeurope.com/rupert-read-the-can-stops-now. See the chapter immediately following this one. (I hasten to add that I was not the organiser of this wonderful walkout. In fact, to my eternal frustration, having spent the year banging the drum for the importance of these final hours of COP26, I had by then caught COVID-19 and was ill in bed, forced to follow events remotely.)

48 Rupert Read, 2021. 'COP26: Why a Bad Outcome "is the Best We Can Hope For', *Euronews* (1 November 2021). Available here: https://www.euronews.com/green/2021/11/01/cop26-why-a-bad-outcome-is-the-best-we-can-hope-for (accessed 8 September 2022).

49 The idea of massive Carbon Dioxide Removal as a tech-fix is dangerous precisely because it tickles the fantasy that says that time is reversible. That there will be irreversible losses if we overshoot and then drawdown is the reality: see e.g., https://www.carbonbrief.org/avoiding-temperature-overshoot-reduces-multiple-climate-change-risks-say-scientists/

50 Ben Webster, 2021. 'Cop26: World Set to Heat Up by 2.7C, Climate Action Tracker Scientists Warn', *The Times* (9 November 2021). Available here: https://www.thetimes.co.uk/article/cop26-world-set-to-heat-up-by-2-7c-says-analysis-of-net-zero-pledges-8mkzd0vsc (accessed 8 September 2022).

51 UNEP, 2021. 'Emissions Gap Report 2021', United Nations Environment Program Report (26 October 2021). Available here: https://www.unep.org/resources/emissions-gap-report-2021 (accessed 8 September 2022).

52 Rupert Read, 2021. 'Rupert Read on 5Live: The Failure of the COP26 Must Be a Wakeup Call', *YouTube* (16 November 2021). Available here: https://www.youtube.com/watch?v=3uynmaxEw0E (accessed 8 September 2022).

53 For instance, Eystein Janesen et al, 2020. 'Past Perspectives on the Present Era of Abrupt Arctic Climate Change', *Nature Climate Change* 2020 (10): 714–721. Available here: https://www.geo.umass.edu/climate/papers2/Jansen_Nature2020.pdf (accessed 8 September 2022).

54 Jasmine Kieft and Jem Bendell, 2021. 'The Responsibility of Communicating Difficult Truths about Climate Influenced Societal Disruption and Collapse: An Introduction to Psychological Research', IFLAS Occasional Papers Vol 7. Available here: http://insight.cumbria.ac.uk/id/eprint/5950/1/Bendell_occasionalpaper7b.pdf (accessed 8 September 2022).

55 See, for example, Ruth Makoff and Rupert Read, 2017. 'Beyond Just Justice: Creating Space for a Future-Care Ethic', *Philosophical Investigations* (1 March 2016): Available here: https://philpapers.org/rec/MAKBJJ-3 (accessed 8 September 2022).

56 Mauro Bolonga and Gerado Acquino, 2020. 'Deforestation and World Population Sustainability: A Quantitative Analysis', *Nature Briefing* (6 May 2020). Available here: https://www.nature.com/articles/s41598-020-63657-6 (accessed 8 September 2022). Or see the reportage by Nafeez Ahmed about hard-headed militaries preparing for such possible eventualities. Nafeez Ahmed, 2019. 'US Military Could Collapse Within 20 Years Due to Climate Change, Report Commissioned by Pentagon Says', *Vice* (25 October 2019). Available here: https://www.vice.com/en/article/mbmkz8/us-military-could-collapse-within-20-years-due-to-climate-change-report-commissioned-by-pentagon-says (accessed 8 September 2022). See also, David Spratt and Ian Dunlop, 2019. 'Existential Climate-Related Security Risk: A Scenario Approach', Breakthrough Institute Policy Paper (May 2019). Available here: https://docs.wixstatic.com/ugd/148cb0_a1406e0143ac4c469196d3003bc1e687.pdf (accessed 8 September 2022).

57 Jonathan Watts, 2021. 'Interview: Climatologist Michael E Mann: "Good people fall victim to doomism. I do too Sometimes"', *The Guardian* (28 February 2021). Available here: https://www.theguardian.com/environment/2021/feb/27/climatologist-michael-e-mann-doomism-climate-crisis-interview (accessed 8 September 2022).

58 Rupert Read, 2022. 'The Inconvenient Truth About Telling the Truth about Climate Breakdown', *ABC* (25 February 2022). Available here: https://www.abc.net.au/religion/rupert-read-inconvenient-truth-about-telling-the-truth/13771202 (accessed 8 September 2022).

59 Alex Brown and National Journal, 2014. 'Here's How NASA Thinks Society Will Collapse', *The Atlantic* (19 March 2014). Available here: https://www.theatlantic.com/politics/archive/2014/03/heres-how-nasa-thinks-society-will-collapse/441375/ (accessed 8 September 2022).

60 Rupert Read, 2022. 'Living in truth in a time of ecological 'emergency' and emergence: Vaclav Havel as eco-guru', *The Ecological Citizen* (7 October 2022). Available here: https://www.ecologicalcitizen.net/article.php?t=living-truth-time-ecological-emergency-emergence-vaclav-havel-eco-guru (accessed 17 October 2022).

61 Don Henley, 2021. 'Few Willing to Change Lifestyle to Save the Planet, Climate Survey Finds', *The Guardian* (8 November 2021). Available here: https://www.theguardian.com/environment/2021/nov/07/few-willing-to-change-lifestyle-climate-survey (accessed 8 September 2022).

62 Chen Zhou, Mark D. Zelinka, Andrew E. Dessler, and Minghai Wang, 2021. 'Greater Committed Warning After Accounting for the Pattern Effect', *Nature Climate Change* (11): 132–136.

63 David Spratt and Ian Dunlop, 2018. *What Lies Beneath: The Understatement of Existential Climate Risk*. Breakthrough Institute Report. Available here: https://www.breakthroughonline.org.au/_files/ugd/148cb0_a0d7c18a1bf64e698a9c-8c8f18a42889.pdf (Accessed 8 September 2022).

64 Climate Change News, 2022. 'We must use Cop27 to transform energy and food systems', *Climate Change News*. Available here: https://www.climatechangenews.com/2022/04/13/we-must-use-cop27-to-transform-energy-and-food-systems/ (accessed 13 October 2022).

65 Bill Hare and Niklas Hohne, 2021. 'Cop26 is Creating False Hope for a 1.5C Rise – the Stark Reality is Very Different', *The Guardian* (10 November 2021). Available here: https://www.theguardian.com/commentisfree/2021/nov/09/cop26-false-hope-climate-analysis-targets (Accessed 8 September 2022).

66 Vaclav Havel, 1986. *Living in Truth*. London: Faber and Faber, p.115.

67 Ibid.

68 Damian Carrington, 2021. ''Blah, blah, blah': Greta Thunberg lambasts leaders over climate crisis', *The Guardian* (28 September 2021). Available here: https://www.theguardian.com/environment/2021/sep/28/blah-greta-thunberg-leaders-climate-crisis-co2-emissions (accessed 13 October 2022).

69 Though of course we should note how imperfect and partial were the 1989 revolutions. And that our task is much harder, because the nature of the system-change that is required is much deeper. Nevertheless, there are genuine parallels that remain, including of course the vitality and centrality of the emphasis on truth-telling. So thinking through the Havelian precedent for us is not, I believe, merely 'hopium'.

70 My thanks to Adam Woodhall, Vlad Vexler, Gail Bradbrook, Atus Mariqueo-Russell and (especially) Marc Lopatin for comments and research that have much enriched this chapter.

71 Rupert Read and Wolfgang Knorr, 2022. 'This is not an 'Emergency'... It's Much More Serious Than That', *Emerge* (21 February 2022). Available here: https://www.whatisemerging.com/opinions/climate-this-is-not-an-emergency-it-s-much-more-serious-than-that (accessed 14 October 2022).

72 https://www.merriam-webster.com/dictionary/emergency

73 Harriet Sherwood, 2019. 'Climate More Pressing Long-Term Issue Than Brexit, Say 71% of Britons', *The Guardian* (26 July 2019). Available here: https://www.theguardian.com/environment/2019/jul/26/climate-more-pressing-than-brexit-say-71-of-britons-poll (accessed 9 September 2022).

74 It's fair to counter that it's not outsourcing to try to get our collective political institutions to reach a particular policy. Saying it's about 'leaders' implies a lack of the sense that we are citizens, with responsibilities and agency. But even as empowered citizens, it is almost irresistible, when looking at dates like 2050, to think that this is something for the future rather than for the now, and to muse that perhaps something or someone will come along meanwhile and 'solve' it for us.

75 Put in philosophical terms: Success looks like a multi-faceted, virtue-ethics-based or deontological or spiritually grounded (*not just* utilitarian/consequentialist) endeavour to prevent further harm and to cope with the damage already unleashed.

76 For explication, see the Conclusion.

77 The real question might be put in this way: Will this new Earth be permanently crippled ('dodo'); will it see a renewed civilisation(s) emerge from ashes ('phoenix'); or might the consciousness-shift that has begun possibly be a little akin to that indicated by Eckhart Tolle in what is probably his most important book, *A New Earth* (London: Penguin, 2005)? That is, might we even manage to transform our failed civilisational paradigm without having to endure the fires of collapse: in my terms, 'butterfly'. (N.B. I will explore the eco-*spiritual* aspect of our predicament and our possibilities in my forthcoming book on eco-spirituality as a rising force in our time.) The answer to this question, of course, may well be complex: it may take centuries to know, and it may well involve quite different trajectories in different parts of the globe. I would caution readers in the Global North not to assume that they will be immune to it. Right now, the climate injustice being perpetrated is rankest against the Global South. But ultimately it is likely to be future generations across the globe who are its profoundest victims. It may turn out that societies such as the USA and the UK are just as or *maybe more* fragile to what is incipiently upon us than, say, East Asian or even West African societies.

78 The 'emergency' framing is really a symptom of a short-termist culture. (Similarly, perhaps, the word 'crisis'.) This is because of the weakness, that I mentioned earlier in this book, of an historical/structural sense in Western culture (with important exceptions in some parts of certain intellectually serious traditions, e.g., Marxism and Catholicism).

79 Rupert Read and Marc Lopatin, 2022. 'Will the Passing of 1.5 Degrees See the End of Cruel Optimism', *Resilience* (8 April 2022). Available here: https://www.resilience.org/stories/2022-04-08/paging-climate-justice-tragically-1-5s-time-is-up/ (accessed 9 September 2022).

80 As detailed in Chapter 10.

81 Ayesha Tandon, 2021. 'Avoiding Temperature "Overshoot" Reduces Multiple Climate Change Risks, Says Scientist', *Carbon Brief* (29 November 2021). Available here: https://www.carbonbrief.org/avoiding-temperature-over-shoot-reduces-multiple-climate-change-risks-say-scientists/ (accessed 9 September 2022).

82 As this book was going to press — too late to change the main text but not too late to add this very last note — Liz Truss became the shortest-serving PM ever. Whether there will be any meaningful change to U.K. policy on climate and nature after she departs — such as an end to U.K. coal and a no-new-oil-and-gas policy — remains to be seen. Don't hold your breath (while they count their money).

83 For more detail, see: https://covidtheplagueyear.wordpress.com/

84 This book, entitled "Transformative adaptation" will appear with Permanent Press in 2023.

85 XR sought creditably to do this, to be a 'teal' (rather than a 'green') movement. (I am referencing here teal consciousness as in spiral dynamics. It is a delicious coincidence that the climate independents who ran successfully against the governing party in Australia recently chose teal as their colour…)

86 Another potentially promising (although risky) development in the political domain, besides that of the emergence of GreensCAN as a possible way forward for the Green Party, is the birth of The Climate Party, a centre-right electoral initiative (i.e., setting up in competition to the Conservatives, just like the teal climate independents did successfully in Australia recently) to whose formative growth and publicity the drive to co-create a moderate flank gave a boost. (It is too soon to say how well The Climate Party will do in relation to the key criterion of truth-telling even where the going gets tough.)
Yet another is Steve Baker Watch, a model (now being copied) of citizen-resistance to climate denying politicians; the Moderate Flank Incubator that I co-direct has given this feisty organisation financial help.

87 As I argue in Why climate breakdown matters, Ipolitics focuses on something that is on balance becoming easier with the sweep of history, while ignoring – worsening – what is becoming harder. Humanism is getting easier and easier; taking seriously the more-than-human, and the long-term, and reaching out across divides of polarisation: these are what have been becoming harder. These are the real challenges, where our civilisation is as of now falling utterly short. Ipolitics orients us in an inopportune way, away from those challenges, and toward the (relatively) easier (not necessarily *easy*!) task of getting society to treat trans people, gay people, black people as equals.

88 To avoid misunderstanding: obviously I am not denying that technological change has an important role to play. The key problem hereabouts is with political economy, which has generally not favoured the best technologies. *Then* (given a change in political economy…) it becomes partly a matter of carrying out the politics/policies which presses all of us to change the pattern of economic incentives (e.g., through a graduated carbon tax, grants for solar panels, a proper Green Investment Bank). However, even if all of this occurred

– which is miles off, in countries like the UK – it would remain important to be clear that technological change even of the right kind is only ever part of what is needed. Crucial too is profound behaviour change, which ultimately means culture change. And in any case, my fundamental point about all this is that it is *too late* to hope for a serene transition; if one was ever possible, it is not, now.

89 By way – as indicated in the latter half of this book – of tapping into the latent sense of having been let down, having had our trust betrayed, having not been kept safe by those charged to keep us safe, nor even by those charged to advise them (and us) on how to keep us (and our kids) safe.

90 This book, entitled "Come as you are: How to build a genuinely inclusive climate movement", will appear with London Publishing Partnership in 2023.

91 Whoever thought it would succeed?! Well, academics, in their touching faith in facts, often did. But it was always basically just a myth to make the lives of intellectuals and academics more cozy. To make us feel more important than we typically are…and to maintain the illusion that by simply doing research in the ordinary way we could play our part in 'solving' any crisis. Of course, a key implication of the failure of this entire model is an embrace of alternative methods of communication: including crucially the arts and 'entertainment'. This is why, increasingly, I am working directly with dramatists, filmmakers, etc. See for instance https://folkfeatures.co.uk/drama-out-of-crisis/ . For the tremendous potential of artistic engagement with the crisis, see my book *A Film-Philosophy of Ecology and Enlightenment* (2019).

92 Rupert Read and Samuel Alexander, 2019. *This Civilisation is Finished.* Melbourne: Simplicity Institute.

93 N.B. Successor radical-flank organisations such as Just Stop Oil have their own, manipulative versions of the 3.5% fetish: such as the fantastical claim that the world can be saved by determined civil resistance for the next three years. (If the reader is irritated that I seem rather down on the radical flank these days, let me say explicitly that I have enduring collegial respect for XR, and for JSO, and that I think there are parts of the radical flank that are doing a splendid job at the radical truth-telling that I call for and aim to instantiate in this book: most notably, Scientist Rebellion.)

94 This is the truth 'they' perhaps most want cancelled. It's why I'm also working on a book called…*The beautiful coincidence.*

95 I owe this point to Alastair Macintosh.

96 Can one 'buy' a being? Not really. But you know what I mean.

97 Big thanks to Victor Anderson and Sarah Kingdom Nicolls for helpful comments on an earlier draft of this Conclusion.

Lightning Source UK Ltd.
Milton Keynes UK
UKHW020126151122
412187UK00012B/399